Calculation vs. Context

Quantitative Literacy and
Its Implications for Teacher Education

The opinions expressed in this volume are those of the authors and do not represent positions or policies of the National Science Foundation, the Johnson Foundation or the Mathematical Association of America.

Figure 2 on page 31: *Handbook of Research on Educational Psychology*, Gustafsson and Undheim, Thomson Gale, 1996, figure 8-5, page 201. Reprinted by permission of David Berliner, Arizona State University.

Figures 3a, 3b, and 3c on pages 31–32: Kit of Factor-Referenced Cognitive Test (KIT) materials are reprinted by permission of Educational Testing Service, the copyright owner. However, the test questions and any other testing information is provided in their entirety by the Mathematical Association of America. No endorsement of this publication by Educational Testing Service should be inferred.

Figure 4 on p. 33: Pope; Simon, Est. of Herbert A., *Human Problem Solving*, ©1972, p. 143. Reprinted by permission of Pearson Education, Inc., Upper Saddle River, NJ.

Figures 2–5 on pages 92–93: *USA Today On-Line Snapshots*. ©USA TODAY, reprinted with permission.

© *2008 by*
The Mathematical Association of America (Incorporated)

Library of Congress Catalog Card Number 2008926250

ISBN 978-0-88385-908-7

Printed in the United States of America

Current Printing (last digit):
10 9 8 7 6 5 4 3 2 1

Calculation vs. Context

Quantitative Literacy and
Its Implications for Teacher Education

June 22–24, 2007
Wingspread Conference Center
Racine, Wisconsin

Edited by

Bernard L. Madison
University of Arkansas
and

Lynn Arthur Steen
St. Olaf College

Published and Distributed by
Mathematical Association of America

Sponsored by

 The Mathematical Association of America's
Preparing Mathematicians to Educate
Teachers (PMET) Project

funded by the

 National Science Foundation

and

THE JOHNSON FOUNDATION
Wingspread Conference Center

Preparing Mathematicians to Educate Teachers (PMET) is funded by DUE-0230847, a grant issued through the National Dissemination Track of the NSF Course, Curriculum and Laboratory Improvement Program (CCLI-ND).

Conference Steering Committee

Stanley Katz, Professor, Woodrow Wilson School of Public and International Affairs, Princeton University; Director, Center for Arts and Cultural Policy Studies; president emeritus of the American Council of Learned Societies.

Bernard L. Madison, Professor of Mathematics, University of Arkansas; President, National Numeracy Network; formerly Dean of the J. William Fulbright College of Arts and Sciences; co-director of Preparing Mathematicians to Educate Teachers.

Robert Orrill, Executive Director, National Council on Education and the Disciplines; formerly Senior Advisor, Woodrow Wilson National Fellowship Foundation; formerly Executive Director of the Office of Academic Affairs at the College Board.

Richard Scheaffer, Professor emeritus of Statistics, University of Florida; Chair, Conference Board for the Mathematical Sciences; formerly President of the American Statistical Association.

Carol Geary Schneider, President, Association of American Colleges and Universities; Ph.D. in history from Harvard University; leader of AAC&U's *Liberal Education and America's Promise, Greater Expectations: The Commitment to Quality as a Nation Goes to College,* and *American Commitments: Diversity, Democracy, and Liberal Learning.*

Lynn Arthur Steen, Professor of Mathematics, St. Olaf College; former President of the Mathematical Association of America; editor of *Mathematics and Democracy*; author of *Achieving Quantitative Literacy.*

Corrine Taylor, Director of the Quantitative Reasoning Program and Assistant Professor of Economics at Wellesley College, President-elect, National Numeracy Network; research on elementary and secondary school finance.

Alan Tucker, Distinguished Teaching Professor of Mathematics, SUNY at Stony Brook; lead author, *Mathematical Education of Teachers,* co-director, Preparing Mathematicians to Educate Teachers.

Contents

Workshop Discussions

Introduction

Introduction

Planning a Conversation about Quantitative Literacy and Teacher Education

Bernard L. Madison[*]
University of Arkansas

Can bad numbers do good?
— From Wingspread discussions

The task was ambitious, some would say hopeless: create a productive two-day conversation among thirty scholars—most strangers to the others—about two virtually disjoint—some would say unrelated—components of US education. One component, teacher education, is a staple of US education, confined in multiple bureaucracies, spread across higher education but governed by schools of education, and firmly entrenched as a national priority. The other, quantitative literacy (QL), has no academic home, is poorly understood and hardly recognized by either academe or the US public, but nonetheless considered important, even critical. And to what end? Better education for QL and for teachers, of course. But what concrete outcomes of the conversation could make a dent in these enormous and operationally unconnected enterprises? Recommendations from much more extensive conversations about narrower issues are often no more effective than shouting into the wind, so even if the

---

[*]Bernard L. Madison is professor of mathematics at the University of Arkansas, having served as department chair (1979–89) and dean of the Fulbright College of Arts and Sciences (1989–99). He has recently directed major NSF-funded national faculty development projects in assessment and the mathematical education of teachers (with Alan Tucker). Having written or edited several articles and books on quantitative literacy and assessment, he is currently writing materials for and assessing learning in a case based course in quantitative reasoning. A native of Kentucky with a Ph.D. degree from the University of Kentucky, Madison was professor of mathematics at Louisiana State University prior to going to Arkansas as department chair.

conversation resulted in an unlikely consensus on what should be done, recommendations to educators and policymakers was not a goal. Rather, beyond the valuable outcome of strangers no longer being strangers, the concrete communal outcome sought was a list of questions that institutions might address to audit their programs of teacher education and QL education: a small beginning step on what is likely a long journey.

The new kid and the old hand …

For a decade a small loosely organized group of interested folks led by historian Robert Orrill had strived to make QL better understood and a priority of both school and college. Some of these were mathematicians, some statisticians, but several other disciplines were also involved. A national forum in 2001 brought together 130 scholars and policy makers to focus on QL education at the juncture of high school and college (Madison & Steen, 2003). Much of the forum discussion tossed about the meaning of QL, where responsibility for QL education lay, and the relationship of QL to mathematics and statistics. The smaller conversation of thirty was to build on this beginning, eventually engaging a larger and more diverse audience.

For a century schools of teacher education had graduated tens of thousands of teachers as US education thrived. But recent international comparisons showing weakness in US education, especially mathematics education, had spurred rethinking of the mathematical education of teachers. One of the glaring weaknesses appeared to be in QL-related areas such as solving contextual problems (OECD, 2003; 2006). Perhaps the time was right for merging the comparatively youthful discussion of QL with the age old but re-invigorated discussion of teacher education.

In this context, the workshop, Quantitative Literacy and Its Implications for Teacher Education scheduled for Wingspread Conference Center in Racine, Wisconsin, June 22–24, 2007, was structured during December 2006 and January 2007 to integrate the recent initiatives on education for QL and the mathematical education of teachers. The QL initiative centered on projects of the National Council on Education and the Disciplines (NCED) over the past decade, which included the 2001 publication *Mathematics and Democracy*. The teacher education initiative grew around publication of *The Mathematical Education of Teachers* report in 2001 by the Conference Board of the Mathematical Sciences (CBMS). Both of these publications emphasize developing habits of mind, one a habit of mind to understand and use quantitative information in everyday life and the other a mathematical habit of mind required to teach mathematics well. Beyond these tangential connections, however, the discussions of mathematical teacher education and QL have had little obvious overlap. The Wingspread workshop was a first step toward synergistic cooperation between teacher education and QL education where teacher education is not restricted to mathematical education.

Why QL and teacher education together …

The obvious reason why teacher education and QL education should be considered together is that K–12 education is responsible for much of QL, and K–12 teachers need to be able to guide students toward QL. Although QL should be an aim of education across all subjects in K–12, a large part of the responsibility falls to K–12 mathematics, which includes data analysis, statistics, and probability. Although part of the aim of the workshop was to elicit support from several disciplines in preparing K–12 teachers better in QL, the primary focus was on the mathematical education of teachers as a means of preparing them as QL educators.

The mathematical education of teachers has received considerable recent attention because there is growing evidence that it can be improved through the collaboration of mathematicians and mathematics educators. Education for QL has received attention because of the growing demands on US residents to understand, utilize, and react to quantitative information and analyses in their daily lives. This growing demand increases the need for stronger quantitative education in K–12 and in college. An important component of the student population for this stronger quantitative education consists of future teachers. Consequently, teacher education and QL education are intertwined in ultimate purpose but loosely connected in educational practice.

Everyday contextual situations are heavily utilized in early school mathematics (and non-mathematics) studies but become much less evident in middle school, high school, and college mathematics. The data analysis, statistics, and probability strand in school mathematics does maintain some everyday contextual connections, but in college statistics courses are usually separate from mathematics courses. Many college statistics courses are methodological or theoretical and have minimal everyday connections. As a consequence of these circumstances, there seem to be advantages from merging the two efforts.

For example, improved mathematical education for teachers results from connecting the mathematics of the college classroom to the mathematics of teaching in school, and QL education is largely about connecting learning and reasoning in mathematics and other college disciplines' classrooms to contextual situations in the contemporary world. Another example is that resolving QL situations requires data analysis and a process similar to the scientific method both of which teachers should understand and utilize. This similarity would provide additional coherence in problem solving in and beyond school. A third example of an opportunity for synergism is to understand the relationship between mathematical proficiency and QL. A very nice model of mathematical proficiency that seems very adaptable to QL is given in *Adding It Up*, where mathematical proficiency is described as five intertwined threads of conceptual understanding, procedural fluency, strategic competence, adaptive reasoning, and productive disposition (Kilpatrick, Swafford, & Findell, 2001).

These and other analogies and connections, plus the opportunistic circumstance of being involved in both the QL and teacher education initiatives, prompted my October 2006 proposal to the Johnson Foundation for the workshop. The proposal had its origin in a small gathering I attended in August 2006. Then Johnson Foundation President Boyd Gibbons invited several people[1] to the Wingspread Conference Center in Racine, Wisconsin, to discuss a series of conferences to craft a new vision of high school through college education from a "clean slate." That discussion, which focused largely on revitalization of undergraduate liberal education, identified several possible conference topics. Among those topics, quantitative literacy was reasonably prominent as a subject for curricular innovation. The proposal for the QL and Teacher Education workshop was a follow-on result largely because of opportunistic funding possibilities, but also because of the potential educational connections and synergisms.

Focusing the conversation …

In order to focus the discussion on QL and teacher education rather than on one or more of the meaning of QL, assessment of QL, liberal education, and assessment of liberal education, the workshop steering committee[2] commissioned seven papers on aspects of QL and teacher education. Three of the seven—on situational learning, teacher certification, and fractions—were directly related to teacher education. In the end we had eight papers[3] since proposed co-authors of the fractions paper, Milo Schield and Alan Tucker, had very different perspectives, so they decided to produce two papers. Historian Robert Orrill and psychologist Neil Lutsky would write on words and numbers—Orrill from the perspective of the humanities and Lutsky on argument and numbers based on experience with a Carleton College initiative. Sociologist Joel Best would address numbers and public policy, British physicist-turned-mathematics-educator Hugh Burkhardt agreed to discuss situated learning, Corrine Taylor investigated the QL needs in business and industry, and Frank Murray would relate QL and teacher certification. The initial drafts of each of these papers were reviewed by at least two workshop participants, and the authors responded to the reviews with a workshop draft. Each paper would be the subject of a session at the workshop, and the authors would produce a final draft in light of these discussions.

With the essays commissioned, the steering committee set about the task of inviting participants. With a dozen of the thirty slots committed to authors and committee members, filling out the participant list for an effective workshop was replete with options. Even though the workshop focused on US undergraduate education, there were numerous relevant perspectives—teacher educators, professional societies, assessment experts, policy makers, undergraduate education specialists, and scholars from the humanities, social sciences, sciences, arts, engineering, business, mathematics, and statistics. Eventually we invited participants from more than a dozen disciplines representing a wide spectrum of interests and expertise.

To move the discussion of QL education forward, the workshop call assumed knowledge of several previous publications on QL and teacher education. These included *Mathematics and Democracy* (Steen, 2001), *Quantitative Literacy: Why Numeracy Matter for Schools and Colleges* (Madison & Steen, 2003), *Achieving Quantitative Literacy* (Steen, 2004) and *The Mathematical Education of Teachers* (CBMS, 2001). In addition, of course, the eight commissioned papers were distributed to participants prior to convening on June 22, 2007.

The workshop program ...

What workshop program would fuel a productive conversation among thirty (eventually this became thirty-one) scholars from multiple disciplines? The commissioned papers provided a foundation, but each participant was expected to have some session leadership role, giving rise to three plenary panels—one highlighting classroom experiences, one on the institutional audit, and the third on influencing the establishment. The eight commissioned papers were discussed in two parallel sequences of two sessions, pairing the two papers on words and numbers, two on fractions, two on situated learning and teacher certification, and two on QL in business and public policy. This was promising, but how would the workshop begin? Who would set the stage for the conversation?

The steering committee agreed on Richard J. Shavelson, Stanford University, who had recently written on his extensive involvement in the innovative Collegiate Learning Assessment. When invited, Professor Shavelson asked how we would suggest that he address the issues of teacher education and QL. To help construct a response to this, one member of the steering committee wrote me describing a recent paper by Shavelson.

> What [Professor Shavelson] gives in that paper is a broad and multidimensional view of the multiple forms of knowledge and related goals of education, juxtaposed with the comparatively narrow focus of commonly used tests on a small part of that broad domain. In fact, he argues that there is a disconnect between what matters most in education and what we are now testing. This, to my mind, draws a broad and radical framework in which to locate teacher preparation broadly (all fields) and specifically (quantitative reasoning). It also sets up especially challenging issues for teacher education since teachers are now pressured to "teach to tests" that are unaligned with the most important uses of knowledge. (Knowing this, what are the ethical responsibilities of educators and higher education overall?) So, I would ask him to spell out the big problem outlined above—offer a few thoughts on teacher preparation—and then share with us his thoughts on how we might create worthy assessments that would be worth teaching to.

Since we were promoting a truly interdisciplinary conversation, we wanted also to relate QL to both pre-professional and liberal education. We turned to Deborah Hughes Hallett who has extensive experience in QL education in mathematics at Harvard University and the University of Arizona, and in public policy at the John F. Kennedy School of Government. She agreed to lead a plenary conversation following Shavelson's presentation to help open up issues for discussion in subsequent sessions.

The two plenary opening sessions, the three panels, the four commissioned paper sessions, and a summing-up session completed the program. The big question remained as to how the papers, the program, and the participants would interact in the inspirational retreat environs of the Wingspread Conference Center.

Summing up: Wingspread would make it work ...

Was the task ambitious or hopeless? Could such a diverse group of thirty-one scholars from more than a dozen disciplines hold a productive conversation on two rather disconnected components of education? The commissioned papers were extraordinary, due largely to the talents and knowledge of the authors rather than guidance from the steering committee, and the papers covered sufficient intellectual ground to underwrite a conversation. The program was set, again with minimal guidance from the steering committee on the contents of the various sessions. In the end, the ingredient that would provide seasoning sufficient for success was the environs of Wingspread[4]. The first words in the program booklet provided the key: "The setting at Wingspread is designed to reduce outside distractions to allow you to focus on the conference issues at hand." Wingspread would provide some of the magic that would make this workshop on QL and teacher education fit its model of "small meetings of thoughtful and rigorous inquiry convened in an atmosphere of candor and purpose."

Needless to say, issues in QL and teacher education constitute an agenda for decades, and a two-day workshop—even in an idyllic and inspirational setting—can only prompt and guide further work. In the article following this, Lynn Steen will focus on what the workshop produced from these and other possibilities.

As the foregoing indicates, developing the workshop involved the attention and work of several people. First, the steering committee members listed in the second endnote and in the front matter of this volume molded the program and commissioned the papers. The commissioned papers were reviewed by at least two workshop participants and at the workshop itself by participants. The high quality of these papers is due to the creativity of the authors and the care and insights of the reviewers. Each workshop participant was assigned a role as session leader, presenter or reporter, and all were carried out splendidly with minimal guidance from the steering committee. My appreciation goes to the Johnson Foundation, its emeritus president Boyd Gibbons, who got me involved in this venture, its current president Roger Dower, and staff members Carole Johnson and Barbara Schmidt. In addition to subsidy by the Johnson Foundation, the workshop was made possible by the NSF-funded PMET project of the MAA. The PMET coordinator at the University of Arkansas, Tami Trzeciak, handled all the pre-workshop communications with participants and the Johnson Foundation staff. Working with co-editor Lynn Steen is always educational and pleasant, and the MAA programs and editorial staff—Michael Pearson, Elaine Pedreira, and Beverly Ruedi—made the volume happen. Thanks.

Special thanks are owed to Robert Orrill whose curiosity, persistence, and deceptively simple questions which defied simple answers launched the QL movement that has now spread to multiple disciplines, scores of campuses, and thousands of students.

References

Steen, L. A. (Ed.). (2001). *Mathematics and democracy.* Princeton, NJ: National Council on Education and the Disciplines.

Madison, B. L., & Steen, L. A. (Eds.). (2003*). Quantitative literacy: Why numeracy matters for schools and colleges.* Princeton, NJ: National Council on Education and the Disciplines.

Steen, L. A. (2004). *Achieving quantitative literacy*. Washington, DC: Mathematical Association of America.

Conference Board of the Mathematical Sciences (CBMS). (2001). *The mathematical education of teachers*. Providence, RI: American Mathematical Society and Washington, DC: Mathematical Association of America.

Kilpatrick, J., Swafford, J., & Findell, B. (Eds.). (2001). *Adding it up*. Washington, DC: National Academies Press.

OECD. (2003). Program for International Student Assessment. Paris, France: Organization for Economic Co-operation and Development (OECD). www.pisa.oecd.org

OECD. (2006). Program for International Student Assessment. Paris, France: Organization for Economic Co-operation and Development (OECD). www.pisa.oecd.org

Endnotes

[1] Andrew Delbanco (Columbia University), Michele Dominy (Bard College), Timothy Fuller (Colorado College), Stanley Katz (Princeton University), Bernard Madison (University of Arkansas), Jerry Martin (American Council of Trustees and Alumni), Russell Newman (University of Michigan), Mark Sargent (Villanova University), Carol Schneider (Association of American Colleges and Universities), and Johnathan Williams (The Accelerated School).

[2] The Steering Committee members were Stanley Katz (Princeton University), Bernard Madison (University of Arkansas), Robert Orrill (National Center on Education and the Disciplines), Richard Scheaffer (University of Florida), Carol Geary Schneider (Association of American Colleges and Universities), Lynn Arthur Steen (St. Olaf College), Corrine Taylor (Wellesley College), and Alan Tucker (State University of New York at Stony Brook).

[3] The eight commissioned papers by Joel Best, Hugh Burkhardt, Neil Lutsky, Frank Murray, Robert Orrill, Milo Schield, Corrine Taylor, and Alan Tucker plus the opening session plenary presentation by Richard Shavelson make up the bulk of this report.

[4] Wingspread was built in 1939, in Racine, Wisconsin. It is the last of Frank Lloyd Wright's prairie houses and his largest single-family residence. Wright designed Wingspread for the family of H. F. Johnson, Jr., who lived there from 1939 to 1959. In 1959, Mr. Johnson established The Johnson Foundation, designating Wingspread as its educational conference center. The Guest House, where conference participants stay, was constructed in 2002.

Reflections on Wingspread Workshop

Lynn Arthur Steen*
St. Olaf College

> *If King Henry the 8th had six wives, how many wives did King Henry the 4th have?*
>
> — Overheard at Wingspread

"Quantitatively oblivious" is how Rhodes Scholar and historian Robert Orrill describes the condition in which his extensive humanities education left him. It also describes roughly half the young adult population of the United States today—although for very different reasons. The experts from a wide variety of fields who gathered in June 2007 at the Wingspread retreat center in Racine, Wisconsin, agreed on little else but this: it is dangerous for democracy if most of its citizens are quantitatively oblivious.

In this brief reflection I call attention to a few of the dozens of issues, concerns, and suggestions that emerged at this workshop, many of which are elaborated and documented in the reminder of this volume. Two special issues dominated the discussions: the relative roles of mathematics vis a vis other disciplines in the development of numeracy, and the potential of teacher preparation as a tool for enhancing numeracy. The issues are subtle, as Orrill's own reflection attests.

---

* Lynn Arthur Steen is special assistant to the provost and professor of mathematics at St. Olaf College in Northfield, Minnesota. Steen has served as an advisor for Achieve, Inc. concerning K–12 mathematics, as executive director of the Mathematical Sciences Education Board, and as president of the Mathematical Association of America. He is the editor or author of many books on mathematics and education including *Math and Bio 2010: Linking Undergraduate Disciplines* (2005), *Mathematics and Democracy* (2001), *On the Shoulders of Giants* (1991), *Everybody Counts* (1989), and *Calculus for a New Century* (1988). Steen received his Ph.D. in mathematics in 1965 from the Massachusetts Institute of Technology.

In addition to giving his own testimony on the relation of humanism and numeracy, Orrill cites evidence from leading twentieth century humanities scholars to suggest that "an aversion to numbers" is deeply rooted in humane studies. Much of this aversion grew out of unease at society's increasing "trust in numbers," to use historian Theodore Porter's apt expression (Porter, 1995). As the standard of civil and political evidence transitioned throughout the twentieth century from the arts and humanities to the natural and social sciences, quantification increasingly replaced classical verities as the foundation of accepted truths. The pretense of objectivity in social measurements rankles humanists still. Echoes of opposition to quantification can be heard throughout higher education even today as faculty argue with administrators and politicians about means of assessing the outcomes of liberal education.

Humanists are not alone in their aversion to numbers. It may come as a surprise to some that many mathematicians have a similar temperament. Berkeley mathematician and educator Alan Schoenfeld called his mathematics education from grade school through Ph.D. "impoverished": no authentic applications, no data other than artificial numbers, no communication other than formal proofs (Schoenfeld, 2001). Although some mathematicians do study numbers, most do not. Instead they employ abstractions in which only the properties of numbers, not the numbers themselves, matter.

My own experience is similar to Alan's. I recall a graduate school class in which the professor in the course of a single hour ran through the entire Latin and Greek alphabets as well as the first few letters of the Hebrew alphabet, but the only numbers in sight were 0, 1, and π. In many years of teaching mathematics to undergraduates, including many future high school and college teachers of mathematics, numbers were rarely of central importance. Since the time of the Greeks, mathematics has been largely about definitions, theorems, and proofs, not numbers, contexts, or measurements. Our heritage is the same as the humanist's, and our disposition is not so much different.

So why, you may wonder, did I become involved with the small band of rebels who have been agitating on behalf of quantitative literacy (QL)? In the early 1990s I was a member of the College Board's advisory committee for mathematics, and for reasons such as those I just outlined we all were mostly oblivious to quantitative literacy. But then the College Board's advisory committee for science began to worry about whether their exams demanded enough mathematical and quantitative acumen to meet the increasing demands for quantification in college science courses. So they asked the mathematics committee for advice on the nature and level of quantitative literacy that would be appropriate to include on the College Board's various science tests.

This question caused some consternation among the mathematicians and mathematics educators on our committee, not least because our first approximation to an answer was mostly disjoint from the topics that we had been advocating be on the College Board's mathematics tests. We were confronted with a dilemma that is still unresolved and that could be heard in many discussions at the Wingspread workshop: Is QL part of mathematics or isn't it? If so, why isn't it taught and learned? If not, who should teach it?

The College Board's response was to publish a series of essays called *Why Numbers Count* (Steen, 1997) that offered a variety of professional views focused, at least indirectly, on the science committee's original question. The leader of this College Board effort was none other than Robert Orrill, no longer quantitatively oblivious. Subsequently, with support from the Pew Charitable Trusts and the Woodrow Wilson Foundation, Orrill led a project intended to make QL a focus of faculty debate on college campuses across the country. The Wingspread workshop is the latest in a series of meetings related to QL that in various ways spun off from these early initiatives.

Has anything changed?

Essays in the current volume—the anchors of the Wingspread workshop—are as diverse and contentious as any of their predecessors. One noticeable change is that QL explorers have moved beyond debates about the definition of QL, not because they reached consensus but because they recognize that development of QL programs is more important (and is also an effective way to clarify definitions). Another change, clearly evident at Wingspread, is that individuals with broader experiences are now awake to the importance of QL and to the potential for connecting to other educational frontiers such as collegiate assessment, general education, and interdisciplinary initiatives. At Wingspread, linkages with teacher education played a central role.

In writing about the licensure of teachers for QL, Frank Murray unwraps layers of formidable complexity in order to disarm anyone who may imagine or suggest simple solutions. Teachers of QL need an extraordinarily diverse set of attributes, including confidence to tackle uncharted quantitative topics, operational skill in mathematical procedures, ability to solve problems that require both deduction and estimation, and experience in contextualizing economic, political and social data. The traditional resource that provides subject knowledge for teachers is the undergraduate major. Yet we now know that even in well established fields such as mathematics, the traditional academic major does not induce in students the kind of deep understanding necessary for a teacher to respond productively to creative conjectures that students readily offer. For a new field like QL—if it even is a "field"—without a major, it appears as if one may need either a miracle or a revolution.

Murray suggests several potential revolutions, including an interdisciplinary major made up of minors from several fields; a major focused on the epistemology of different fields; a great books major centered on seminal texts (not textbooks!) in several fields; and a cognitive psychology major focused on how the mind matures in comprehending different kinds of knowledge. It will take years of trials to see how well any ideas such as these may do in developing for the kind of QL knowledge that teachers need to be ready with apt examples, useful analogies, and constructive questions.

The other traditional component of teacher preparation, typically more contentious, is the cluster of courses and experiences (practice teaching) that focus on pedagogy more than content. Murray recounts the appeal of naïve teaching, that is, the natural instinct that all people have to teach what they know to others, to justify restraints on this component of teacher education. Since QL has not ever been an organized discipline, and is often overlooked by subjects that are organized as disciplines, much of what people learn in this domain comes from such naïve sources. Evidence shows, however, that teachers operating in this instinctive mode (primarily showing and telling) tend to have low expectations for students of different backgrounds and are inattentive to higher order understanding of the kind characteristic of QL. Untrained teachers have great difficulty, for example, with recognizing the value of productive student efforts that nonetheless yield incorrect results.

For a variety of reasons, public pressure for more and better teachers coupled with skepticism about the education establishment has led to a multiplicity of approaches to teacher licensure. In this environment, Murray argues, the effort to increase the level of quantitative literacy in the schools will surely fail unless all aspects of licensure are addressed and coordinated, including clarity about the assessable features of numeracy, establishment of an appropriate undergraduate major, new requirements for the teaching license, redesign of license tests, recognition in accreditation and state approval standards, and incorporation in the state's curriculum assessments. Without these, Murray warns, "the policy levers provided by teacher education, licensing, credentialing, and accreditation are relatively powerless to provide a structure that will support QL."

Is there any hope?

Murray's analysis pretty much buries the option of QL as a thriving K–12 discipline. However, this may not matter much since most QL advocates have not sought to go down that road. The predominant recommendations for QL seem to be either cross-disciplinary (e.g., like writing across the curriculum) or sub-disciplinary (e.g., within mathematics, rather like statistics now often is). But Murray appears to say more, namely, that unless QL takes on all the trappings of a discipline—standards, majors, assessments, licensure—it cannot grow within the K–12 scene.

Others seem more hopeful. For instance, Shoenfield—having recovered from his "impoverished" mathematics education—now believes that QL and the contents of school mathematics should be "largely overlapping." Richard Scheaffer, former president of the American Statistical Association, is "convinced" that quantitative literacy has a rather large overlap with statistics education, especially as the latter is being defined and developed for the K–12 mathematics curriculum (see, for instance, www.amstat.org/education/gaise/). Henry Kepner, president-elect of the National Council of Teachers of Mathematics, reports that QL is largely consistent with current mathematics standards and curricula, largely because data analysis, statistics and probability "has entered the main stream" of school mathematics. Kepner notes, however, that QL depends far more on the processes of mathematics—reasoning, communication, representation, connections, and problem solving—than do typical mathematics standards (which focus on skills and content).

Physicist-turned-mathematics-educator Hugh Burkhardt argued similarly at Wingspread in his paper on QL for all. He sees QL as a "major justification" for the large slice of curriculum time given to mathematics and argues that QL can be a powerful learning aid for mathematical concepts, particularly for those who are not already high achievers. Moreover, he avers, teaching QL well is mathematically demanding, even for mathematics teachers; those less well-prepared "could not cope."

Following much the same line of thinking as Murray, Burkhardt notes further that it is extremely difficult to establish and sustain cross-curricular teaching. "If QL is not taught in mathematics, it will not happen." However, he warns against the common pro-QL argument made by some mathematics educators that for most students, thinking mathematically about problems from everyday life offers powerful support for sense-making in mathematics:

> However true, this is an extraordinarily inward-looking view. For me and, I believe, for most people, the *practical* utility of being able to *think mathematically about practical problems* is the prime motivation for studying mathematics; its inherent beauty and elegance are merely a welcome bonus (author's italics).

Regrettably, Burkardt continues, among teachers of mathematics, there is too-often an unfortunate correlation between "knowing more mathematics and having an inward-looking view of it."

In his paper on critical thinking about public issues, sociologist Joel Best makes a similar argument about inward-focused mathematics, but draws from this observation an opposite conclusion. According to Best, educators teach mathematics as a series of what he calls increasingly complicated "calculations," by which he means all of the methods (e.g., arithmetic, equations, deduction) by which mathematical problems "are framed and then solved."

> Because mathematics instruction is organized around principles of calculation, calls for quantitative literacy tend to assume that students are not sufficiently adept as calculators, and that they need to improve their calculating skills, that they either need to beef up their abilities to carry out more sophisticated calculations or that they need to become better at recognizing how to apply their abstract calculation skills to real-world situations.

This preoccupation with calculation is Best's explication of the inclination towards inwardness that worries Burkhardt. Whereas Burkhardt seeks to draw QL into mathematics to save it from its inward tendencies, Best argues that QL requires issues of "construction" that move well beyond the boundaries of mathematical calculations:

> Humans depend upon language to understand the world, and language is a social phenomenon. In this sense, all knowledge is socially constructed. … In particular, numbers are social constructions. Numbers do not exist in nature. Every number is a product of human activity: somebody had to do the calculations that produced that figure. Somebody had to decide what to count, and how to go about counting.

This is not a mundane observation, says Best, especially when numbers frame public issues. Understanding such figures requires far more than calculation (that is, mathematics). To be quantitatively literate, students need to appreciate the process of social construction. Needless to say, this is not a skill in which mathematics teachers are trained and few are good at it.

Several Wingspread participants (mostly non-mathematicians) appeared to share this sentiment. "Why associate QL with mathematics?" asked psychologist Neal Lutsky. "Mathematicians are least well prepared to deal with the meaning of socially constructed numbers, which is the essence of QL." Indeed, the much-heralded goal of teaching mathematics in context is by definition out of context when done in a mathematics class. It is also very difficult to do there since mathematics students come from all sorts of different contexts. Perhaps contextual teaching—the essence of QL—really belongs where the context is the primary subject being taught.

Assessment expert Richard Shavelson adds yet a further caution. One suggestion often heard at Wingspread (and earlier) is to add QL to teacher education programs. Shavelson warns that even if it could be achieved, this proposal does not get at the heart of the problem, in part because "K–12 teachers are not the cause of the problem." The proposal, he claims, ignores the current policy and social contexts of education in the U.S. The policy context is one of high stakes testing:

> This form of accountability drives what gets taught by teachers in the classrooms. Unless QL becomes a central focus of what is meant by mathematics achievement, and this is very unlikely, it will be put aside even if we accomplished our goals with teachers.

The social context, Shavelson continues, is one of a society that largely does not possess, foster, or support QL. Most U.S. adults are not quantitatively literate. Many believe that mathematical and quantitative abilities are determined by birth (some have the "right stuff" and others do not). Worse, recent developmental data cited by Shavelson suggests that resistance to scientific and quantitative reasoning will arise and persist in children when such reasoning leads to conclusions that clash with prior expectations or with views championed by trusted adults. Thus it is that society's aversion to things quantitative is transmitted from generation to generation.

All these strands, and more, lead Shavelson to suggest that the proper response to the crisis of QL is not a special focus on QL for prospective and practicing teachers, but a broad focus on QL for all students, especially at the introductory college level. This route, indirect rather than explicit, will perforce include future teachers. Moreover, aspects of embedded QL are included in one of the most promising new tools for assessing liberal education, namely the Collegiate Learning Assessment (see www.cae.org/content/pro_collegiate.htm).

Interestingly, Orrill makes a similar suggestion with regard to students and teachers of the humanities: instead of forcing on them what their culture has traditionally viewed as repugnant, proponents of QL should invite humanists to use their own texts as a foundation for revisiting their stance toward quantification:

> Humanists are more likely to enter the conversation—and remain involved—if they can begin on familiar ground. At the same time, this also would bring QL into contact with documents and texts about which it so far has had little to say. Here, then, might be found the makings of a genuine conversation.

As Orrill recognizes, no one can predict whether such a conversation would be a productive undertaking. Current circumstances, he believes, suggest that the time is right to try. "Many humanists now are calling for a thoroughgoing reconsideration of humanistic practice; this self-questioning could open new, if still untried, paths through the academic hedgerows."

But can we communicate?

A second major theme that emerged from many Wingspread discussions was the obvious observation that quantitative literacy is a type of literacy—or in modern jargon, communication. Indeed, "communicating effectively about quantitative topics" emerged as a high priority need from virtually every source that economist Corrine Taylor studied in her analysis of what the business world wants in the way of QL. These sources expressed other needs as well, foremost being the habit of guessing and checking for reasonableness, known informally as "thinking for oneself," and experience with messy "cases" requiring a decision rather than only textbook problems with specific correct solutions.

One might say that mathematics is to QL as template problem solving is to authentic decision making. In the former, textbook exercises provide exactly the information needed to solve the problem—no more and no less; in the latter, the relevant data are typically both incomplete and contradictory. Many school mathematics teachers, by their own testimony, decided to pursue mathematics because they like to follow rules, and are most comfortable with the precision and definitiveness of a good mathematics problem. To help their students become quantitatively *literate,* mathematics teachers will need to encourage argument and discussion, just like English and history teachers do. That's a tall order. But to the extent that it succeeds, it would also help students become better mathematicians.

Discussion and debate about messy cases would surely help develop the strong communication skills about quantitative issues that experts say are keys to success in the business world. According to Taylor's findings, businesses strongly believe that their success depends on individuals "who can communicate with others on a team about assumptions, techniques, results, and decisions." Retired General Electric engineer William Steenken affirmed the importance of these skills in engineering also. "It's not only differential equations, but the ability to talk precisely and clearly about their work."

Psychologist Lutsky makes a similar case in his paper "Arguing with Numbers." His foundation, however, is not the needs of business but of liberal education. Based on work he and his colleagues have done with students at Carleton college, Lutsky opines that "the construction, communication, and evaluation of arguments" is a fitting context for quantitative literacy. In many situations, quantitative reasoning is an essential ingredient in the "framing, articulation, testing, principled presentation, and public analysis of arguments." In even more instances, QL is supportive although not central in making or critiquing an argument. Thus QL becomes an imperative for liberal education, both in high schools and colleges.

Many have suggested that "writing across the curriculum" is an appropriate model for QL: it recognizes the multi-disciplinary character of QL, honors the contextual differences among disciplines, and is a practical way to enlist relatively large numbers of advocates from different departments. The success of writing across the curriculum is an inspiration to those who hope QL will follow in these footsteps. Indeed, the National Numeracy Network (see www. math.dartmouth.edu/~nnn) is loosely modeled after the National Writing Project, a nationwide system of local coalitions that has provided effective support for writing across the curriculum for over a quarter century. In 2008, the NNN launched a new electronic journal *Numeracy: Advancing Education in Quantitative Literacy* (see services.bepress.com/numeracy).

While not disputing the possibilities of QL across the curriculum, Lutsky adds a unique twist: instead of working across the whole curriculum, focus on the teaching of writing:

> Quantitative literacy can be usefully situated in the context of argument, in the presentation of statements supporting claims. In this sense, arguments are not only reasons to take one position or another on a contentious issue but address ... claims about the nature of a phenomenon or the importance of a topic. Teaching students how to identify and find the constituent elements of an argument, how to organize arguments systematically, ... how to present arguments clearly and meaningfully, ... how to address their own arguments reflectively, and how to evaluate others' arguments are fundamental to education at all levels and in almost all disciplines.

By examining a wide variety of papers that college students wrote for courses across the curriculum, Lutsky and his colleagues discovered that a third of these papers failed to use quantitative reasoning when it should have been central to the analysis, and nearly nine in ten failed to use QL when it was peripheral but of potential benefit to the argument. Clearly, there is much potential for QL within courses that stress written (and oral) analyses.

Statistician Milo Schield puts his finger on one possible reason why so many students write papers absent potentially helpful quantitative reasoning: most do not know how to express simple quantitative ideas in clear English. Many will confuse, for example, the percentage of males who are smokers with the percentage of smokers who are male. In one study, 20% of college students were unable to read a 5th grade pie graph showing percentages of smokers divided by religion (protestant, catholic, other). Notwithstanding the ubiquity of tables and graphs in popular media such as *USA Today*, translating the meaning of numbers and percentages that appear in such tables into correct English is beyond the ability of all but a small minority of even college-educated adults. It seems plausible to infer from the widespread inability to express correctly the meaning of such numbers a corresponding inability to understand their meaning.

Schield's paper is one of two devoted to fractions, the tormentor of millions of school children (not to mention of educated adults). He focuses on the needs of the 40% of college students who major in non-quantitative subjects. These students, he notes, are more likely than their quantitatively-oriented classmates to become journalists, policy advocates, lawyers, opinion makers and political leaders, thereby influencing local and national policies. Schield advances the rather radical proposition that to improve quantitative literacy and attitudes towards mathematics, it makes sense to deemphasize fractions for these students and focus more on percentages and rates. He asks, pointedly, why should they be burdened with mastering the arithmetic of mixed fractions ($1/3 + 2/7$) when so many cannot even translate a simple proportion into clear English? Isn't it more important to emphasize understanding the multiple representations of fractions in tables, graphs, proportions, percentages, and ratios than to focus on manipulating numbers which for all too many students demonstrably convey no meaning?

Good questions, all. Applied mathematician Alan Tucker empathizes. Too many students, he notes, fall off the ladder of mathematical learning in the transition from whole number arithmetic to fractions. Like Schield, Tucker offers his own catalog of horrors, such as the fact that given a choice of 1, 2, 42, or 45 as approximate values of $19/20 + 23/25$, a majority of U.S. eighth graders chose 42 or 45. These students, Tucker observes, "did not think of a fraction as a number."

Whereas Schield worries that students do not know what a fraction *means*, Tucker worries that that they do not know what it *is*. That distinction about summarizes the archetypal difference in approaches that distinguish social scientists from mathematicians. Students, of course, need to know both what a fraction is and what it means. For adults, it is probably more important that they remember what it means.

Tucker urges that children be introduced to fractions first via *unit fractions* such as ½, ⅓, and ¼. For young children, he says, unit fractions evolve naturally from counting numbers: if a pie is divided into equal fourths, the pieces when counted yield a total of 4. In this way, unit fractions can be thought of as a type of counting number known as *reciprocals*. They fit easily into the various counting activities in which young children engage as they learn about numbers.

Then at the earliest appropriate age, Tucker says, children should be told that a *fraction* is a "number that is an integer multiple of some unit fraction." For example, ¾ means $3 \times ¼$, where ¼ is a number with the property that four of them add up to 1 (a "unit" in mathematical jargon). Of course, in real elementary classrooms, these spare definitions would be supported by a variety of examples from everyday life such as telling time, making change, cooking, sharing portions, and measuring small quantities.

For mathematicians, the decision to define fractions in terms of unit fractions solves a major conceptual problem, namely, establishing that a fraction is a number. The logical chain from counting number to unit fraction to (ordinary) fraction satisfies the mathematician's sense of definitional clarity. Some children—not all, but an important cohort—will also appreciate this clarity. Others, at least, may find that it helps avoid unnecessary confusion.

Tucker identifies a second less obvious advantage of defining fractions this way: it makes clear that the numerator and the denominator of a fraction represent different things. Numerators are standard counting numbers, while denominators are a totally new quantity, namely, reciprocals. This distinction, the theory goes, will help students overcome the strongly held belief that numbers must be whole numbers, and that fractions are not numbers but rather just part of something.

A third advantage elucidated in Tucker's paper, is that unit fractions help clarify the distinction between fractions and division: a fraction is a number that may be the answer to a particular division task. Confusion arises because after the early grades, we use the fraction notation (¾) to mean both the number ¾ and the arithmetic problem $3 \div 4$.

Finally, and perhaps most important for QL, unit fractions focus attention on the role of units (e.g., miles, feet, inches) as mediator between an abstract number (¾) and a real context (¾ mile), and on the way rates are used to convert from one type of unit to another. Changing from miles to feet is much like changing from thirds and fourths to twelfths when seeking a common denominator in order to add $\frac{1}{3} + \frac{1}{4}$.

Despite their vastly different approaches, Schield and Tucker share a common concern that current schooling is strikingly deficient in achieving a primary goal of middle school mathematics, namely to convey the interrelated meanings of fractions, percents, proportions, decimals, ratios, and rates. For several centuries many of these topics were collected under the "rule of three" (given any three numbers, find the fourth); until the beginning of the twentieth century, the rule of three (and some Euclid) was all the mathematics expected of students entering American colleges.

Kepner noted that one reason for the decline in comprehension of these topics by high school graduates in the last half century is that teachers taught them according to the different algorithms required for calculation rather than as different perspectives on a common topic. No wonder most adults do not recognize fractions, ratios, and percents as three representations of the same thing: even when well learned, they appear as they were taught: as three distinct notations, each with distinct rules for calculation. One can see from this tidbit of pedagogical history why the "calculation" perspective, as Best put it, is totally inadequate to meeting the interpretive needs cited by Taylor, Schield, and Tucker.

So what's next?

Although mathematics plays a central role in the relentless recent increase in student testing, no one ever seems to ask why. Parents and politicians take for granted that mathematics is essential for work, for college, and for informed living. Even the once-oblivious Orrill now argues that

> if individuals lack the ability to think numerically, they cannot participate fully in civic life, thereby bringing into question the very basis of government of, by, and for the people (Orrill, 2001).

Whereas humanists in the late 19th century warned against the idolatry of large numbers that politicians used to praise the ever-expanding American life, a century later we find numbers have penetrated every aspect of social, political, economic, and cultural life. Now not only our economy but also our democracy depends on numbers.

But is the numeracy we need to guard our democracy the mathematics found on required school tests? I think it is fair to say that virtually every Wingspread participant would answer this question in the negative, though not all for the same reason. Some would say the tests do not reflect good mathematics; others that good mathematics is not effective numeracy; still others that numeracy cannot be tested in this manner. But every participant would also recognize that teachers and students have little choice but to focus on the high-stakes tests as they are. This is what Shavelson calls the ignored policy context of education.

Fortunately, higher education has so far escaped the deluge of narrowly focused tests, and the assessment options currently being explored (e.g., CLA) are very compatible with the goals of quantitative literacy. Even though some might wish that students' QL needs would be met by their secondary education, it seems clear from the analyses at Wingspread that the most creative and effective forces for QL will be those in postsecondary education.

Higher education is in many ways exactly the right place for QL to develop and diversify. As a nation we are blessed with an extraordinary variety of institutions—public and private, large and small, two and four year, college and university—all of whom actively innovate in order to compete for students. Many very different QL projects are already underway in postsecondary institutions. I would anticipate that as ideas from Wingspread become known more widely, some of the issues debated there will take shape in the form of pilot programs on different campuses. The infrastructure to support this work is already in place—within mathematics, via the MAA's Special Interest Group for QL (see www.maa.org/sigmaa/ql), across disciplines via the National Numeracy Network, and on the web via the new electronic journal *Numeracy*.

Of course, higher education is not without its own impediments. Academic silos, entrenched curricula, state articulation agreements, academic guild requirements—not to mention recalcitrant tenured professors—will keep the campus QL rebels well occupied. They will not have the luxury of a "clean slate" as the earlier Wingspread meeting had hoped. But they now have momentum: energetic leaders, active programs, and budding professional associations.

Should QL be part of a college's mathematics requirement or organized across the curriculum with "Q" courses in many departments? Might it be integrated into Comp 101 as part of every freshman's initial exposure to college writing? Do students in non-quantitative tracks need QL, or do their current requirements suffice? What should be done for college students who do not know what fractions are or mean?… The list of questions is endless, more than enough to fill the agenda of the next numeracy workshop.

References

Orrill, R. (2001). Mathematics, numeracy, and democracy. In L. A. Steen, *Mathematics and democracy: The case for quantitative literacy* (pp. xii–xx). Princeton, NJ: National Council on Education and the Disciplines. www.maa.org/Ql/fm13-20.pdf

Porter, T. M. (1995). *Trust in numbers: The pursuit of objectivity in science and public life*. Princeton, NJ: Princeton University Press.

Schoenfeld, A. (2001). Reflections on an impoverished education. In L. A. Steen, *Mathematics and democracy: The case for quantitative literacy* (pp. 49–54). Princeton, NJ: National Council on Education and the Disciplines. www.maa.org/Ql/049-54.pdf

Steen, L. A. (1997). *Why numbers count: Quantitative literacy for tomorrow's America*. New York, NY: The College Board.

Keynote Presentation

Reflections on Quantitative Reasoning: An Assessment Perspective

Richard J. Shavelson[*]
Stanford University

If we seek to enhance the quantitative reasoning of the American public, not only do we need to be able to say what quantitative reasoning is, we also need to know how to teach for it and how to measure progress toward the QR goal. My focus is on assessment, but inevitably I also need to address definitional questions. Moreover, teaching and assessing go hand-in-hand. So what is said about assessment has application to teaching (and vice versa).

From an assessment perspective the first question that arises about QR is: "What is the construct to be measured?" Or, "What is the 'theory' or 'model' of QR from which an assessment emanates?" This question conjures up over 100 years of study of quantitative reasoning. Psychometric, cognitive, and situated theories all have something to say about the question. An early task, therefore, is to set forth a simple assessment framework that provides the structure for the paper—what is to be measured, with what tasks, and with what inferences? Once the framework is sketched, I will introduce definitional questions and set forth a particular definition that constrains what we might assess and how we might assess it.

---

[*]Richard J. Shavelson is the Margaret Jack Professor of Education, Professor of Psychology, Senior Fellow in the Stanford Institute for the Environment, and former I. James Quillen Dean of the School of Education at Stanford University. He served as president of the American Educational Research Association; is a fellow of the American Association for the Advancement of Science, the American Psychological Association, and the American Psychological Society; and is a Humboldt Fellow. He is completing a book entitled (tentatively): *The Quest to Assess Learning and Hold Higher Education Accountable*. His other books include *Statistical Reasoning for the Behavioral Sciences*, *Generalizability Theory: A Primer* (with Noreen Webb), and *Scientific Research in Education* (edited with Lisa Towne). *E-mail*: richs@stanford.edu

With a working definition of QR in hand, the assessment question turns to what kinds of tasks might be used to measure the construct. Two approaches to measuring QR—one with roots in behaviorism and the other from cognitive and situative perspectives—illustrate different underlying conceptions of learning, knowing, and performing. They lead to different answers to the question of what tasks should be used to measure QR. As we will see, certain kinds of tasks are likely to elicit quantitative reasoning in a manner consistent with our definitional view, while other kinds of tasks are less likely to do so. One approach that I like—akin to cognitive/situative orientations—is reflected in the new Collegiate Learning Assessment (CLA). Consequently, I describe it in some detail to illustrate one important direction for assessment of QR that may fit what the field is looking for.

With the assessment built, the final question that arises is, "How justifiable is the inference from test information to students' or teachers' level of quantitative ability?" Due to space limitations, I only note but do not discuss the need to amass empirical evidence and the kinds of evidence that support a QR interpretation. In concluding, I examine from a variety of perspectives the potential for teacher preparation and enhancement to improve QR, thereby raising questions as to whether teacher education in QR is the most effective approach to deal with this 21st century challenge.

Approaching quantitative reasoning through assessment

There is a growing consensus that to function effectively in the 21st Century, Americans need to be "quantitatively literate," that is, be able to think and reason quantitatively when the situation so demands. And by implication, Americans certainly need to be able to quantitatively reason better than they can today. This view is clearly expressed in the invitation letter for this conference: "The goal of the conference is to explore educational solutions to the increasing quantitative reasoning demands on US residents."

If we seek to enhance the quantitative reasoning of the American public, we need not only to be able to say what quantitative reasoning is, we also need to know how to teach for it and how to measure progress toward the QR goal. This paper focuses on assessment of quantitative reasoning. But assessment, strangely enough, is a good road into the topic because it forces us to be clear about what we mean by QR, what kinds of tasks or activities would elicit QR (both in the classroom and on the assessment), and what kinds of evidence is needed to convince ourselves we are measuring the "right stuff."

Perhaps surprisingly, the way assessment developers approach the development of measures of any construct like QR is instructive not just for assessment, but also for teaching and learning. Development work is guided by an assessment triangle (NRC, 2001) shown in Figure 1. The construct vertex represents the "thing" or "concept" or "construct" we want to measure. In our case, the construct is quantitative reasoning. That is, we want to infer the level of quantitative reasoning displayed by an individual or group of individuals based on our assessment. To do so means we have to begin by defining what we mean by QR. Such a definition is not set in stone. Rather, as we gain experience teaching QR and empirical evidence about the adequacy of our assessment of QR, we may very well modify the definition. But such a working definition is a starting point.

The observation vertex of the triangle represents the kinds of *activities* we believe would permit an individual or group to display QR. The definition of the construct helps define a universe of possible activities—tasks and how they might be responded to—that we might use to assess QR... *or to teach QR!* The definition also rules out some activities that we would not consider as counting as eliciting the kind of QR we have in mind. Typically we do a kind of task analysis to insure, at least logically, that the tasks/ responses that form the activities on the assessment are drawn from the universe of QR activities that we intend to draw inferences to, based on assessment scores.

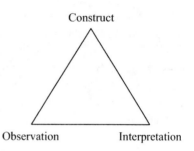

Figure 1. The assessment triangle.

Finally, the interpretation vertex focuses on the *inferences* we make from a sample of activities to the universe of activities that we want to know about a person in order to capture his or her QR. By interpretation is meant the basis for scoring performance and the chain of reasoning—logical, cognitive, and statistical—that links the scores on the assessment to the construct of interest, QR. Indeed, we do not know what an assessment measures unless we know what the tasks are, how people are asked to respond to those tasks, and how those responses are scored. And even then we need logical, cognitive, and statistical evidence that supports our interpretation that we are really measuring the QR we set out to measure. Given limited time, this vertex will not be discussed herein further.

I hope by now I have convinced you that the assessment process demands a great deal of reasoning, especially *quantitative reasoning!*

Definitions of quantitative reasoning

Historically, within psychology and education, there have been three approaches to defining QR: psychometric (behavioral roots), cognitive (mental
process roots) and situative (social-contextual roots). Each sheds light on what
we might or might not mean by QR. And, as we will see, current definitions
of QR in the mathematics QR community overlap some combination of the
cognitive and situative here.

Psychometric Approach

The psychometric approach begins with a "mini-theory" of what QR might be
and then builds tests to match that theory. It then tests the theory empirically,
looking for patterns of correlations among test scores such that tests measuring QR should correlate higher with each other than with tests of, say, verbal
or spatial reasoning. This tradition has been ongoing for more than 100 years.
There seems to be consensus that there is strong evidence for a "QR factor" in
the sense that people's performance on QR tests can be distinguished clearly
from their performance on other tests. QR "... requires reasoning based on
mathematical properties and relations. The reasoning processes may be either
inductive or deductive, or some combination of them" (Carroll, 1993, p. 239).
QR tests have titles such as "Arithmetic, Necessary Arithmetical Reasoning
and Mathematical Aptitude." Carroll goes on:

> Typically these tests present a variety of mathematical reasoning
> problems such as word problems (solving verbally stated mathematical
> problems), number series, and problems requiring selection of
> appropriate arithmetical operations. Generally, the amount of actual
> numerical computation required is small. [S]cores are expected to
> depend mainly on the level of difficulty in the problems that can be
> performed.

To put QR in context, a figure generated by Snow and Lohman (1989,
p. 318, Figure 3.13) and adapted by Gustafsson and Undheim, (1996, p. 201,
Figure 8-5) is helpful (Figure 2). This "dartboard" representation of human
cognitive abilities shows the bull's eye to be general mental ability. Radiating
out from the center are verbal, spatial, and quantitative reasoning. Let us focus
on the QR piece of the board (or slice of pie). As we move away from the bull's
eye toward the edge of the board, the tests of QR become increasingly like
those tasks that might be taught in school and, consequently, most influenced
by education. This said, those tests closer to the bull's eye seem to best reflect
what psychometricians think of as QR.

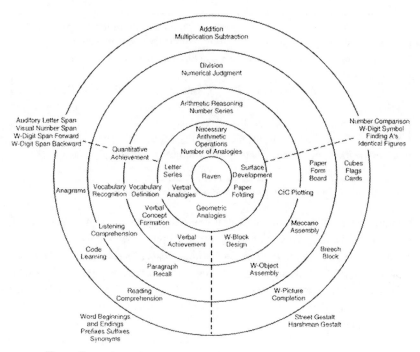

Figure 2. A schematic "dart-board" model of human cognitive abilities

To get a better feel for some of these tests, questions from two QR tests are presented in Figures 3a, 3b, and 3c. The test question in Figure 3a, taken

---

Example II. Chairs priced at $40 each are being sold in lots of 4 at 85% of the original price. How much would 4 chairs cost?

    1 - divide and add   3 - subtract and divide
    2 - multiply and multiply   4 - multiply and divide

One way to solve the problem would be to multiply $40 by .85 and then multiply this product by 4; therefore you shoud have put an x through the number 2. (Although some problems may be solved in more than one way, as with Example II, only the operations of one of these ways will be given among the options).

When 2 operations are given, they are always given in the order in which they should be performed.

Your score on this test will be the number marked correctly minus a fraction of the number marked incorrectly. Therefore, it will *not* be to your advantage to guess unless you are able to eliminate one or more of the answer choices as wrong.

Figure 3a. Necessary Arithmetic Operations Test

In this test you will be asked to solve some problems in arithmetic. Work each problem and put an x on the number in front of the answer that you choose.

Example: How many candy mints can you buy for 50 cents at the rate of 2 for 5 cents?

      1- 1   2- 20   3- 25   4- 100   5- 125

The correct answer to this problem is 20. Therefore, you should have marked an x through the number 2 to indicate the correct answer

Your score on this test will be the number marked correctly minus a fraction of the number marked incorrectly. Therefore, it will not be to your advantage to guess unless you are able to eliminate one or more of the answer choices as wrong.

Figure 3b. Arithmetic Aptitude Test

from the Necessary Arithmetic Operations Test (Ekstrom, French, Harman, & Dermen, 1976), falls close to the bull's eye in Figure 2 while the test question in Figure 3b, taken from the Arithmetic Aptitude Test (Ekstrom, French, Harman, & Dermen, 1976), falls just beyond. For completeness, Figure 3c shows the Addition Test (Ekstrom, French, Harman, & Dermen, 1976) which falls at the periphery of the dart board and is closely tied to education and practice.

The questions in Figure 3a and b, then, appear to be consistent with Carroll's claim that the tests do not place a high demand on computation but rather focus on reasoning with numbers, operations, and patterns. The last question focuses on numerical speed and accuracy, not what is meant by QR in the psychometric view of cognitive abilities.

You are to write your answers in the boxes below the problems. Several practice problems are given below with the first one correctly worked. Practice for speed on the others. This practice may help your score.

Practice Problems:

4	7	12	84	7	34	17	45	31	80
9	6	5	54	38	81	50	41	52	78
1	15	67	72	80	51	74	89	19	15

[14] [ ] [ ] [ ] [ ] [ ] [ ] [ ] [ ] [ ]

Your score on this test will be the number of problems that are added correctly. Work as rapidly as you can without sacrificing accuracy.

Figure 3c. Addition Test

Cognitive Approach

Psychometicians have focused on observed *performance* or *behavior* in response to a set of similar test questions seeking to understand the *structure of abilities* underlying consistency in responses to these questions. In contrast, cognitive scientists assume that performance on cognitive tests can be divided into component processes and ask about the *cognitive operations* that underlie the observed performance on psychometric and other tasks. Or, as John Anderson put it, "Most of the research in psychometrics has focused only on whether a person gets a question right or not. In contrast, information-processing [cognitive] analyses try to examine the steps by which a person decides on an answer to such a question and the time necessary to perform each step" (2005, p. 447). Cognitive scientists' goal is to extract sets of elementary processes that underlie a wide range of cognitive functioning and thereby describe elemental cognitive processes.

With respect to QR, cognitive scientists (actually seldom) ask, "What kinds of reasoning processes or steps are brought to bear in responding to QR type tasks? In what order? And for how long?" Unfortunately, QR has not been a focus of much cognitive research (although deductive and inductive reasoning have). One possible example (Figure 4) is cryptarithmetic (Newell & Simon, 1978, p. 143):

Although not the best example of QR, cryptarithmetic does provide a sense of the cognitive scientists' approach in analyzing a potential QR task. They begin by setting forth the task environment— the affordances and constraints of the problem—for a single problem. They then analyze, logically and mathematically, the possible solution paths

DONALD   D = 5
+ GERALD
ROBERT
Here each letter represents a digit (0, 1,...,9) and you know D = 5; no other letter equals 5. What digits should be assigned to the letters such that, when the letters are replaced by their corresponding digits, the sum above is satisfied?

Figure 4. Cryptarithmetic

for the problem. The next step in the analysis is to move from this intensive analysis of a single task to an extensive analysis which generalizes the rules for solving one problem to other problems that fall in the same domain. They then observe human performance on the task, asking problem solvers to "think aloud" to capture the reasoning processes underlying task completion. In this way, they map the "problem space" that the problem solver has constructed and the step by step processes used in problem solving. They may then test their conclusion by building and testing computer models of problem solving.

This approach, then, has less to say about constructing assessment activities than it does about how to determine whether the assessment activities tap the kind of thinking—QR—of interest. Cognitive methods, such as the think-aloud technique, provide important means for examining proposed interpretations of assessments purporting to measure QR.

Situated Approach

While psychometricians ask, figuratively, "How fast will the car go?", and cognitive scientists ask "How does the engine make the car go fast?", situativists ask "How is the car used in a particular culture?" Situativists ask about *person-in-situation*. They view performance as influenced in part by what the individual brings to a situation and in part by the physical and social situation—its affordances and constraints—in which that performance becomes meaningful. In their pursuit of understanding human abilities, including QR, they also want to know how a particular culture affects the development and use of these abilities.

Indeed, situativists would probably frame the question of understanding QR a bit differently than has been done here. They would begin by *not* assuming that QR resides solely within the person but would view QR within a *community of practice*—e.g., those individuals engaged in culturally relevant activities in which reasoning quantitatively is demanded and the various resources of the community would be brought to bear on those activities. They would view a person accomplished in QR as having the capacity to engage others in working together to think critically, reason analytically and to solve a problem, for example. Cognitive abilities, from this perspective, reside *in a community of practice*.

To pursue the situative perspective further is a task for another time, as the capacity to assess performance poses a very real challenge for this perspective. And issues of credibility arise when those outside the situative community of practice are asked to buy into the way they assess performance.

That said it is possible to conceive of tasks that fit to some degree with this perspective. For example, the use of case studies in business which among other things demand QR, as Corrine Taylor (2007) points out, seems consistent with the situative perspective. QR is embedded in the larger set of real-world constraints and affordances and the problem solution depends upon them. Moreover, Bernie Madison's (2006) characterization of QR in contrast to mathematics resonates with this perspective (Figure 5). QR, from his perspective, is carried out in real-life, authentic situations; its application is in the particular situation, one dependent upon context including socio-politics. The problems are ill defined, estimation is crucial, and an interdisciplinary approach is often needed

Mathematics	Quantitative Reasoning
Power in abstraction	Real, authentic contexts
Power in generality	Specific, particular applications
Some context dependency	Heavy context dependency
Society independent	Society dependent
Apolitical	Political
Methods and algorithms	Ad hoc methods
Well-defined problems	Ill-defined problems
Approximation	Estimation is critical
Heavily disciplinary	Interdisciplinary
Problem solutions	Problem descriptions
Few opportunities to practice outside the classroom	Many practice opportunities outside the classroom
Predictable	Unpredictable

Figure 5. Contrast between mathematics and quantitative reasoning.

Perhaps the following question, from Friedman's statistics book, also falls within the situative perspective and what it means to reason quantitatively:

One of the drugs in the Coronary Drug Project was nicotinic acid. Suppose the results on nicotinic acid were as reproduced below. Something looks wrong. What, and why?

	Nicotinic Acid		Placebo	
Group	Number	Deaths	Number	Deaths
Adherers	558	13%	1813	15%
Non-adheres	487	26%	882	28%
Total	1045	19%	2695	19%

Answer: About half of those getting Nicotinic Acid adhered to their treatment regimen whereas two-thirds of those getting the Placebo adhered to their regimen. This suggests something went wrong. For instance, the Nicotinic acid may have had unpleasant side effects or the Placebo tasted better. In short, it may not have been a true placebo.

Note that the exercise does not involve formulas (other than noticing the large difference in adherence rates).

These examples of situated QR seem also to fit with the Mathematical Association of America's notion of QR; all students who receive a bachelor's degree should be able to:

- Interpret mathematical models such as formulas, graphs, table, and schematics, and draw inferences from them.
- Represent mathematical information symbolically, visually, numerically, and verbally.
- Use arithmetical, algebraic, geometric, and statistical methods to solve problems.
- Estimate and check answers to mathematical problems in order to determine reasonableness, identify alternatives, and select optimal results.
- Recognize that mathematical and statistical methods have limits.

The definition that seems most productive from a present day notion of QR is that of the situativists, perhaps augmented by a cognitive analysis. With this in mind, approaches to measuring QR provide striking contrast.

A possible approach to measuring quantitative reasoning

The tasks used to elicit quantitative reasoning and how that reasoning is expressed in overt performance derives from the construct definition. The psychometric perspective's definition of QR is helpful in thinking about the kinds of activities that might be included on a QR assessment—activities that require reasoning based on mathematical properties and relations. However, this perspective's translation of the definition into assessment activities is constrained by the behaviorist notion that a complex task can be divided into component parts and then put back together again. Consequently, the questions found on psychometric tests are pretty much context free and posed in the form of multiple-choice test questions, as we saw in Figures 3a–c. This claim is reinforced by the GRE QR section (ETS, 2002). Carroll (1993) considers the GRE Quantitative scale to be prototypical of QR.

The kind of question in Figure 5, typical of the approach to measuring QR in the U.S., appears on many of the 30 or so QR websites I looked at having been provided a mere 1,800,000 to consider by Google. These questions appear

---

The average (arithmetic mean) of x and y is 20. If $z = 5$, what is the average of x, y, and z?

        A. 8 ⅓   B. 10   C. 12 ½ D. 15   E. 17 ½

Answer: Since the average of x and y is 20, $(x + y)/2 = 20$ so $x + y = 40$. Thus $x + y + z = 40 + 5 = 45$, and therefore $(x + y + z)/3 = 45/3 = 15$.

Figure 5. Problem-solving question from the GRE released questions.

to draw on some aspects of QR. However, such questions, by their content and format (multiple-choice), seem context free in nature with one correct answer actually provided among a set of alternatives. Such an approach does not appear to be what many faculty and the MAA expect to see on a test of QR.

Rather, the situated approach seems to capture current thinking about QR. That is, QR is evidenced when confronted with a well contextualized, messy, open-ended, "real-world" task that demands analysis, critical thinking, problem solving and the capacity to communicate a solution, decision, or course of action clearly in writing. For example, two pieces of information provided in Figure 6 are part of an "in-basket" of information given to the problem-solver. The task smacks of the "real world" with substantial contextualization. The evidence points to a possible correlation between growth in sales of the SwiftAir aircraft and an increase in accidents—was the increase proportional? There are a number of solution paths and more than one solution to the problem could be justified.

The Collegiate Learning Assessment (CLA) provides one possible example of an assessment that fits a situated notion of QR. It poses complex tasks, provides a variety of information (e.g., data, graphs, research review article, news paper article, op ed piece) and asks students to review the material, determine what material is relevant and what irrelevant, and arrive at a problem solution, decision, or course of action that is justified based on the evidence in hand. There is no single correct answer but a variety of possible answers that vary in their credibility and evidentiary base.

Given all of the information in the document library, what do you think are the three most likely causes of the accidents described in Document 3? Justify your answer with information from the document library.

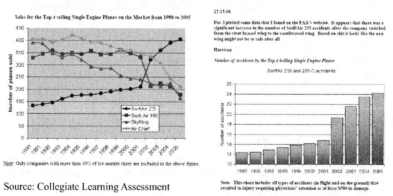

Source: Collegiate Learning Assessment

Figure 6. Possible situated QR problem—two pieces of information regarding SwiftAir sales and accidents as part of an in-basket of information.

Because the CLA comes close to the situated definition of QR and what might be sought in an assessment of QR, the next section describes the CLA in some detail. In passing, note that the kinds of tasks used on the CLA would make excellent teaching activities. If faculty used these activities as part of their teaching, students might be more likely than at present to improve their reasoning. One caveat is in order. The CLA contains a number of performance tasks that demand among other things QR. But it is not a test of QR. The CLA is presented here as an example of an assessment that might very well be adapted to focus on QR. That said, philosophically it fits well with situated QR notions in that QR is more than quantitative reasoning; it involved an entire complex of reasoning and so do the CLA tasks.

Characteristic	Attributes
Open-ended Tasks	• Tap critical thinking, analytic reasoning, problem solving and written communication • Realistic work samples • Engaging task as suggested by alluring titles such as "brain boost," "catfish," "lakes to rivers") • Applicable to different academic majors
Computer Technology	• Interactive internet platform • Paperless administration • Natural language processing software for scoring students written communication • Online rater scoring and calibration of performance tasks • Report institution's (and subdivision's) performance (and individual student performance confidentially to student)
Focus	• Institution or school/department/program within institutions • Not on individual student performance (although their performance is reported to them confidentially)
Sampling	• Samples students so that not all students perform all tasks • Samples tasks for random subsets of students • Creates scores at institution or subdivision/program level as desired (depending on sample sizes)
Reporting	• Controls for students' ability so that "similarly situated" benchmark campuses can be compared • Provides value added estimates—from freshman to senior year or with measures on a sample of freshmen and seniors • Provides percentiles • Provides benchmark institutions

Figure 7. Characteristics of the Collegiate Learning Assessment

The roots of the CLA can be traced to progressive notions of learning, focusing on critical thinking, analytic reasoning, problem solving, and written communication (Figure 7; Shavelson, 2007a,b). These capabilities are tapped in realistic "work-sample" tasks drawn from education, work, and everyday issues. They are accessible to students from the wide diversity of majors and general education programs. The capacity to provide these rich tasks without overburdening students is afforded by recent developments in information technology. The assessment is delivered on an interactive internet platform that produces a paperless, electronic administration and online report of results. Written communication tasks are scored using natural language processing software and performance tasks are currently scored by online human raters whose scoring is monitored and calibrated. Within the next year, the performance tasks will be scored as well by computer software.

The assessment is divided into three parts—analytic writing, performance tasks, and biographical information—the first two of which are relevant to present discussion. Two types of writing tasks are administered. The first, make an argument, invites students to present an argument for or against a particular position. For example, the prompt might be: "In our time, specialists of all kinds are highly overrated. We need more generalists – people who can provide broad perspectives." Students are directed to indicate if they agree or disagree and to explain the reasons for their positions. In a similar vein, the second type of writing task (Figure 8) asks students to evaluate an argument (CLA, 2005).

The CLA performance tasks present real-life problems to students such as that for Dyna-Tech and Crime (Figures 9 and 10) by providing an "in-basket" (or nowadays, "computer basket") of information bearing on the problem (CLA, 2005). Some of the information is relevant, some not; part of the problem is for the students to decide what information to use and what to ignore. Students

---

A well-respected professional journal with a readership that includes elementary school principals recently published the results of a two-year study on childhood obesity. (Obese individuals are usually considered to be those who are 20 percent above their recommended weight for height and age.) This study sampled 50 schoolchildren, ages 5–11, from Smith Elementary School. A fast food restaurant opened near the school just before the study began. After two years, students who remained in the sample group were more likely to be overweight—relative to the national average. Based on this study, the principal of Jones Elementary School decided to confront her school's obesity problem by opposing any fast food restaurant openings near her school.

Figure 8. Collegiate Learning Assessment "Evaluate An Argument" Example.

You are the assistant to Pat Williams, the president of DynaTech, a company that makes precision electronic instruments and navigational equipment. Sally Evans, a member of DynaTech's sales force, recommended that DynaTech buy a small private plane (a SwiftAir 235) that she and other members of the sales force could use to visit customers. Pat was about to approve the purchase when there was an accident involving a SwiftAir 235. You are provided with the following documentation:

1. Newspaper articles about the accident
2. Federal Accident Report on in-flight breakups in single engine planes
3. Pat's e-mail to you & Sally's e-mail to Pat
4. Charts on SwiftAir's performance characteristics
5. Amateur Pilot article comparing SwiftAir 235 to similar planes
6. Pictures and description of SwiftAir Models 180 and 235

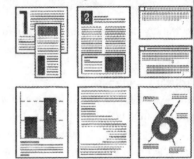

Please prepare a memo that addresses several questions, including what data support or refute the claim that the type of wing on the SwiftAir 235 leads to more in-flight breakups, what other factors might have contributed to the accident and should be taken into account, and your overall recommendation about whether or not DynaTech should purchase the plane.

Figure 9. Collegiate Learning Assessment Performance Task (DynaTech)

integrate these multiple sources of information to arrive at a problem solution, decision, or recommendation. Students respond in a real-life manner by, for example, writing a memorandum to their boss analyzing the pros and cons of alternative solutions and recommending what the company should do. In scoring performance, alternative justifiable solutions to the problem and alternative solution paths are recognized and evaluated.

A closer look at the Crime Performance Assessment provides insight into what a CLA type QR performance assessment might include. Students are posed the problem, provided an in-basket of information, and asked to analyze the information critically and then inform Mayor Stone about their conclusions with evidentiary justification. The in-basket contains the following information:

- Newspaper article about crime in the community
- Research abstracts about drug education program
- Report about success of a drug education program in another community
- Police report (with table of data) about crime and drug use in the community

Pat stone is running for election as mayor of Jefferson, a city in the state of Columbia. Mayor Stone's opponent in this contest is Dr. Jamie Eager. Dr. Eager is a member of the Jefferson City Council. You are a consultant to Mayor Stone. Dr. Eager made the following three arguments during a recent TV interview. First, Mayor Stone's proposal for reducing crime by increasing the number of police officers is a bad idea. "It will only led to more crime." Dr. Edgar supported this argument by showing that counties with a large number of policy officers per resident tend to have more crime then those with fewer officers per resident. Second, Dr. Eager said "we should take the money that would have gone to hiring more policy officers and spend it on the XYZ drug treatment program." He supported this argument by referring to a news release by the Washington Institute for Social Research that describes the effectiveness of the XYZ drug treatment program. Third, Dr. Eager said that because of the strong correlation between drug use and crime in Jefferson, reducing the number of addicts would lower the city's crime rate. He showed a chart that compared the percentage of drug addicts in a Jefferson zip code area to the number of crimes.

Mayor Stone has asked you to prepare a memo that analyzes the strengths and limitations of each of Dr. Eager's three main points, including any holes in those arguments. Your memo also should contain points, explain the reasons for your conclusions, and justify those conclusions by referring to the specific documents, data, and statements on which your conclusions are based.

Figure 10. Collegiate Learning Assessment Performance Task (Crime)

- Plots of the relationship between police offers and crime
- Private investigator report about possible connection between opponent and drug education program

In-basket items on a QR assessment might look like those from CLA's crime task described in Figure 11.

QR and teacher education

In his letter of invitation to this conference, Bernie Madison noted that, "The goal of the conference is to explore educational solutions to the increasing quantitative reasoning demands on US residents, with special focus on the education of teachers." Apparently one such solution is in hand—add QR to the teacher-preparation and teacher-enhancement agenda. Certainly this can be done. And CLA-type assessments might be used to check to see if teachers have met some expected level of QR—although even if they did, the whole question of pedagogical-content knowledge and classroom practice then needs to be dealt with. That is, can teachers translate their QR into classroom learning

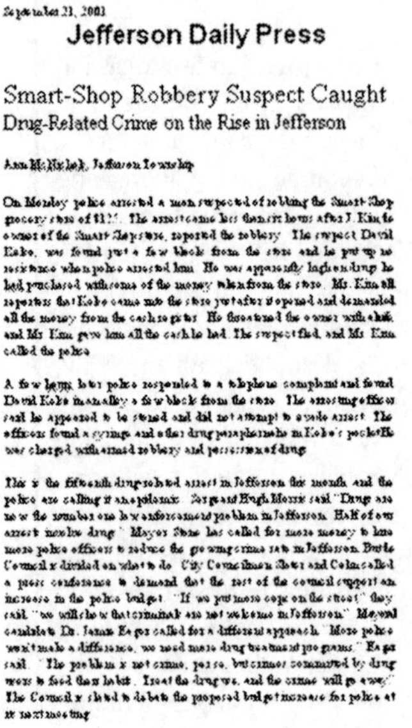
Jefferson Daily Press

Smart-Shop Robbery Suspect Caught

Drug-Related Crime on the Rise in Jefferson

Crime Rate and Drug Use in Jefferson
By Zip Code

Zip Code	Percent of Population Using Drugs	Number of Crimes in 1999
11510	1	10
11511	3	20
11512	5	90
11520	8	50
11522	10	55

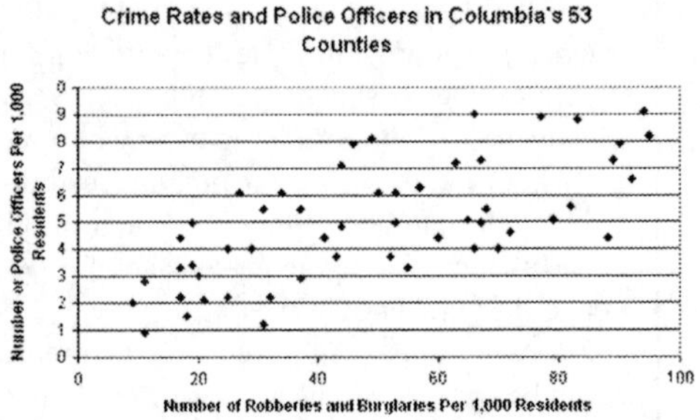
Crime Rates and Police Officers in Columbia's 53 Counties
Number of Police Officers Per 1,000 Residents
Number of Robberies and Burglaries Per 1,000 Residents
0
20
40
60
80
100

Figure 11. Collegiate Learning Assessment performance task: Some in-basket information (Crime).

environments where students can acquire the knowledge, skills and abilities that constitute QR?

As may be evident, I am not sanguine about this proposal. The proposal does not get at the heart of the problem—and K–12 teachers are not the cause of the problem. The proposal ignores the current policy and social context of education in the U.S. The policy context is one of high stakes testing. This form of accountability drives what gets taught by teachers in the classrooms. Unless QR becomes a central focus of what is meant by mathematics achievement, and this is very unlikely, it will be put aside even if we accomplished our goals with teachers.

The social context is one of a society that largely does not possess, foster or support QR. That message is broadcast loud and clear, especially to students. The belief about QR goes something like this. QR and mathematics achievement in the U.S. are part of birth—your fixed ability—and some have the right stuff and others do not. (I do not agree with this.) Moreover, the teaching of mathematics K–16—pedagogy, curriculum, context, students—has not met the challenge of creating a quantitatively literate citizenry. Even more strikingly, the existence proof is all around us. In other countries students achieve a much more sophisticated understanding of and ability to do mathematics. International comparisons have made this very clear.

In an article just published in the journal, *Science*, Bloom and Weisberg (2007, p. 996) provide a cogent basis for explaining the U.S. context:

> The developmental data suggest that resistance to science [and QR!] will arise in children when scientific claims clash with early emerging, intuitive expectations. This resistance will persist through adulthood if the scientific claims are contested within a society, and it will be especially strong if there is a nonscientific alternative that is rooted in common sense and championed by people who are thought of as reliable and trustworthy.

Since this is a meeting of higher educators, it seems appropriate to lay part of the QR problem at our feet. A study by Liping Ma (1999) highlights the problem. She compared U.S. and Chinese elementary mathematics teachers teaching of mathematics. The U.S. teachers were college graduates; not so the Chinese teachers. Nevertheless, the latter were found to have a strong conceptual grasp of mathematics and emphasized the conceptual in their teaching while the latter had an algorithmic grasp and emphasized algorithmic practice in their teaching. The simple algorithms understood by U.S. teachers were inadequate to the task—e.g., judging when a novel approach taken by a student to a problem was justified. A similar finding, contrasting US and Japanese elementary mathematics teachers, has been reported by Aki Murata (2004). Moreover, in my experience, students who indicate that they will pursue a teaching credential while earning a bachelor's degree in an academic major may take a somewhat different pattern of courses than "regular" majors. If this pattern is common in mathematics departments, there is then an opportunity-to-learn issue.

If we are not preparing college students adequately in mathematics and quantitative reasoning, perhaps a significant part of the QR problem lies not in teacher preparation but in the preparation of students generally, and teachers in the academic majors. If this chain of reasoning (admittedly not quantitative!) makes any sense, perhaps we should be talking about preparing QR in introductory college mathematics courses for the broad college audience, in general education courses, and in the mathematics major creating a pedagogy that gives the diversity of students access to both QR and the level of mathematics needed to teach in high school.

I understand this is heresy. But perhaps it will stimulate discussion broadly and lead to an analysis of the various contributors to the current state of QR in our country. In the end, we may settle on teacher education. But perhaps if we do, we will have done so with some perspective.

References

Bloom, P. & Weisberg, D. S. (2007). Childhood origins of adult resistance to science. *Science,* 316:5827, 996–997.

Carroll, J.B. (1993). *Human cognitive abilities: A survey of factor-analytic studies.* New York, NY: Cambridge University Press.

Collegiate Learning Assessment in Context. (2005). New York, NY: Council for Aid to Education. www.cae.org/content/pdf/CLA.in.Context.pdf.

Ekstrom, R., French, J., Harman, H., & Dermen, D. (1976). Manual for kit of factor-referenced *cognitive tests,* Princeton, NJ: Educational Testing Service.

Educational Testing Service. (2002). *Preparing for the verbal and quantitative sections of the GRE General Test: Sample questions with explanations.* Princeton, NJ: Author www.ets.org/Media/Tests/GRE/pdf/011499.GRE.pdf.

Gustafsson, J.-E., & Undheim, J.O. (1996). Individual differences in cognitive functions. In D. Berliner & R. Calfee (Eds.), *Handbook of educational psychology* (pp. 186–242). New York, NY: Macmillan.

Ma, L. (1999). *Knowing and teaching elementary mathematics: Teachers' understanding of fundamental mathematics in China and the United States.* Mahwah, NJ: Lawrence Erlbaum & Associates.

Madison, Bernard. (2006). Presentation to the Northeast Consortium on Quantitative Literacy, Annual Meeting, Amherst College, April 29, 2006.

Murata, A. (2004). Paths to learning ten-structured understanding of teen sums: Addition solution methods of Japanese Grade 1 students. *Cognition and Instruction, 22(2).* 185–218.

National Research Council. (2001). *Knowing what students know: The science and design of educational assessment.* Washington, DC: National Academies Press.

Newell, A., & Simon, H.A. (1972). *Human problem solving.* Englewood Cliffs, NJ: Prentice Hall.

Shavelson, R. J. (2007). *A brief history of student learning: How we got where we are and a proposal for where to go next.* Washington, DC: Association of American Colleges and Universities.

Shavelson, R. J. (2007a). Assessing student learning responsibly: From history to an audacious proposal. *Change,* 39(1), 26–33.

Snow, R.E., & Lohman, D.F. (1989). Implications of cognitive psychology for educational measurement. In R. Linn (Ed.), *Educational measurement,* 3rd ed. (pp. 263–331). New York, NY: Macmillan.

Taylor, C. (2008). Preparing students for the business of the real (and highly quantitative) world. This volume (pp. xx–yy). Washington, DC: Mathematical Association of America.

Commissioned Papers

Humanism and Quantitative Literacy

Robert Orrill[*]

> *The President of Harvard College, seeing me once by chance*
> *soon after the beginning of a term, inquired how my classes*
> *were getting on; and when I replied that I thought they were*
> *getting on well, that my men seemed to be keen and intelligent,*
> *he stopped me as if I was about to waste his time. 'I meant,'*
> *said he, 'what is the number of students in your classes.'*[1]
>
> —George Santayana,
> *Character and Opinion in the United States*

With some hesitation, I invite you to consider Santayana's simple parable. This brief remembrance is one that he first recounted in a lecture delivered in England near the end of WWI. The incident itself, however, happened many years before, in the early 1890's, when Santayana was a junior member of Harvard's philosophy department. The impatient (and here unidentified) president in the story is Charles Eliot who, at the time this encounter took place, was widely regarded as the most influential educator in the United States. Although they are colleagues, there is no cordiality indicated in the meeting of the two men. Nor, almost three decades later, is there even a hint of any in its recollection.

---

[*] Robert Orrill is the Executive Director of the National Council on Education and the Disciplines. Among other academic and teaching positions, he was most recently the Senior Advisor at the Woodrow Wilson National Fellowship Foundation, and Executive Director of the Office of Academic Affairs at the College Board. He has organized and edited numerous publications on American education, including *The Future of Education: Perspectives on National Standards in America* (1994), *The Condition of American Liberal Education: Pragmatism and a Changing Tradition* (1995); and *Education and Democracy: Re-imagining Liberal Learning in America* (1997). Following undergraduate study at Purdue University, Robert Orrill was a Rhodes Scholar at Worcester College, Oxford. He currently resides in Solebury, PA. *E-mail:* rorrill8@comcast.net

The absence of good feeling in this encounter is, I believe, an emotional fact worth our close attention. In its details, of course, the incident does not seem to present a quantitative problem of any difficulty or interest. Hence my hesitation in calling it to your attention. Indeed, we know from other sources that Santayana would have had no trouble supplying the number that Eliot demanded from him. At this time, he tells us, the students in his classes numbered no more than a handful—there were only three or four undergraduates, for instance, in a course on the British Enlightenment that he had inherited from William James. So, in a strict sense, there is no quantitative issue here that involves anything other than the most rudimentary arithmetic.

Is this a case, then, in which Quantitative Literacy (QL) has little or no work to do? The answer depends, I believe, on how much we should make of the claim that QL informs us about numbers, not in the abstract, but in the many ways we meet them in life itself.[2] Here, for instance, what occurs in this encounter amounts to much more than an exchange of quantitative data. In Eliot's mind, as the young Santayana knows, three or four students in a class translates directly into a moral judgment—in sum, it means not enough, too few, a weak showing. Moreover, it further signifies that Santayana is failing to do his share and, very possibly, may be making less than a full effort. Taken in context, therefore, the number in question cannot be understood apart from its moral reverberations. In effect, numbers and feelings are so closely joined as to be inseparable and thereby combine in this instance, as they so often do in life, to make a moral event. How, if at all, should QL approach such events? Only arithmetically? Or is it attentive to them in a more complete sense and, if so, to what end? Addressing these questions here at Wingspread might help clarify the role of QL in a liberal education.

Here, in the beginning, something more might be said about Santayana's meeting with President Eliot. Briefly stated, what happens in this encounter? Outwardly, of course, very little. By chance, the two men come together, exchange a few words, and then go their separate ways. Inwardly, however, much changes for the young Santayana. Suddenly, he finds that the world is very different from what he thought it to be. In effect, the question that Eliot puts to him conveys that the worth of philosophy—or any subject—should be derived from the number of students that it can attract. For Santayana, this intrusion of market standards rendered the environment almost unrecognizable. What, innocently, he had believed to be a sanctuary of the intellect now confronts him—in the person of the president—with a setting dominated by the rule of quantification and a crude regime of numbers. From one moment to the next, then, his own alma mater, Harvard, had become a strange and oppressive place.

If he noticed Santayana's discomfort at all, it is unlikely that Eliot felt it to be of any significance. Doubtless, he considered the question he asked to be of the utmost importance and entirely in order. Writ large, in fact, it reflected a policy of "quantitative aggrandizement" then evident everywhere in American education.[3] In promoting this policy, Eliot himself had warned that the very survival of the American college depended on its keeping pace "with the growth of the country in population and wealth."[4] This meant, in practice, that the college must seek to have more of everything—money, students, buildings—and to gain these things it, above all, must include "all subjects" in its offerings and leave the choice among them entirely open to the election of students. Without a prescribed curriculum of its own, then, nothing could narrow a college's chances for growth. No matter that an absence of any uniformity in the learning of students made it difficult to give "clear meaning" or ascribe "exact significance" to the baccalaureate degree. For this, too, Eliot had a quantitative solution. As it had in the past, he said, the degree should still testify to the "main fact" that "the recipient has spent eight or ten years, somewhere between the ages of twelve and twenty-three, in liberal studies."[5]

Although much more could be said, this perhaps is where we should leave the Eliot-Santayana encounter. Suffice it to note that Santayana's discomfort in the American academic environment only intensified during the years that followed this incident. With a sense of profound relief, he eventually fled Harvard and thereafter rejected all offers either to return there or to accept a chair in any other American university. Moving on, though, I now want to discuss how this case is an illustrative one. Examining the historical record, we can see that many of Santayana's contemporary humanists shared the same feelings of discontent with Eliot's "new education;" and this, I believe, helps account for why they gave quantitative matters so little consideration in their approach to student learning. Without much exaggeration, one could even say that they entirely banished quantitative issues from their vision of a liberal education.

This, I might add, was essentially the character of my own educational experience. As an undergraduate, my studies were mostly of a humanistic nature; and, looking back, I cannot recall even once being asked to address a serious quantitative question in completing a large array of courses devoted to history, literature, philosophy, and the arts. This surely contributed to my becoming quantitatively oblivious; and later, as a teacher myself, I in turn never asked my students to attend to any of the quantitative problems lurking in the texts that we read together. Until very recently, in fact, I do not think that I noticed that they were there.

My own experience, then, suggests that an aversion to numbers has a long history in the so-called humane studies. Why this antipathy to quantification?

What is its origin? In part, at least, its beginnings can be traced to the "anxiety" felt by Anglo-American humanists when, in the late 19th century, they looked ahead to the looming dominance of a mass democracy.[6] As they saw it, this threat of an overwhelming deluge of numbers placed civilization itself in grave peril. In 1884, for instance, Matthew Arnold delivered a lecture in the United States that he entitled "Numbers; or the Majority and the Remnant." His main intent in this address was to warn his listeners about the dangers of becoming enthralled by the large numbers that made up so much of the data typically brought forth in praise of American life. To be sure, he said, these facts were undeniable and seemingly very impressive. Citing a fellow countryman, he told his listeners:

> The vast scale of things here, the extent of your country, your numbers, the rapidity of your increase, strike the imagination, and are a common topic for admiring remark. Our great orator, Mr. Bright, is never weary of telling us how many acres of land you have at your disposal, how many bushels of grain you produce, how many millions you are, how many more millions you will be presently, and what a capital thing this is for you.[7]

This, of course, is said ironically. In plain speech, Arnold means that all this talk of abundance is tiresome stuff. Worse yet, such boasting about material things weighs heavily on the spirit and is deadening to the soul.

More sermon than lecture, Arnold's talk holds fast throughout to a single message. The Americans may be a people of plenty, he says, but morally this has placed them at risk of identifying goodness with quantity—that is, of mistaking more for better and most for better yet. For correction, therefore, they should look to the lessons of tradition, to the wisdom that resides—as he famously put it—in "the best which has been thought and said." There they will be reminded that the "sages and saints" always have warned that the multitude is "unsound" and not to be trusted. More positively, they also will find the teachings that make up "the doctrine of the *remnant*." This guidance conveys the good news that a few, an elect, can protect against the failings of the many and spiritually uphold an entire culture. In some variant or other, of course, this belief that the masses should (and will) allow themselves to be led by a priesthood or an elect of some kind would long continue to influence the evolution of American education.

During his lecture tour, Arnold also emphasized that the doctrine he preached had a direct bearing on educational arrangements in the United States. It meant that the aim of the university, above all else, should be to nurture this much-needed "saving remnant." In turn, this task required that the work of the university should be devoted to the transmission of tradition and, therefore, that study therein should attend to a core curriculum that was literary, classical, and morally earnest in its orientation. Rejecting any such dwelling on the past, Eliot had said that the university should seek its fortune in the here and now, embrace American life, and grow along with it. Arnold, in contrast, urged that this teeming activity be kept out of collegiate education. Both held that students should be led "to think," but, for Arnold, thought was reflective, a turning inward, and directed in each person toward development of a "best self." If study remained true to this aim, the university could hope to produce a leavening cadre of "workers for good." Necessarily, of course, such an approach envisioned an exalted role for both faculty and students. For the sake of the culture at large, they were to serve as nothing less than a clergy of the intellect and keepers of the spirit.

In essence, what Arnold advocated was a somewhat spiritualized version of an Oxbridge college. During the years that followed, this in fact became the model that most humanists favored and hoped would prevail in American undergraduate education. More than any other option, this ideal provided their own basis for self-understanding and sense of vocation. They knew, of course, that their views were in conflict with the utilitarian model promoted at this time by Eliot and most other university presidents. In a concrete instance, we glimpsed this clash in the Eliot-Santayana encounter. On a larger scale, this also was the drama that Henry James saw unfolding when, in 1904, he revisited Harvard after an absence of twenty years. An admirer of Arnold, he had hoped on his return to find something resembling an American Oxford—quite literally, as he put it, to walk into a cloistered haven "inaccessible…to the shout of the newspapers, the place to perambulate, the place to think, apart from the crowd." In contrast with Eliot, then, he thought that Harvard should provide an "antidote" to the life that surrounded it. The image he invoked was that of a "university…stamped with the character and function of the life-saving monasteries of the dark ages."[8]But, instead, what he found happening on the ground was a dimming of this ideal. This weakening, moreover, was not due to the world pressing in and encroaching upon Harvard. On the contrary, much to James' regret, he saw that a "restlessly expansive Harvard" had acquired an impetus of its own and was now actively "stretching forth, in many directions, long, acquisitive arms."

The humanists, then, had wanted the American college to remain enclosed and be kept small. By 1900, however, most of them recognized that this was a lost cause. Enrollments in college were increasing almost everywhere; and the prevailing educational policy opposed all efforts to place limits on growth. With few exceptions, the humanists acquiesced in the face of these dominant trends; but they remained uncomfortable with the conditions that resulted. They were puzzled, most especially, by student motives for attending college. Why were they coming in ever-mounting numbers and what were they seeking? The answers to these questions turned out to be perplexing. All too few students, it seemed, shared the faculty outlook on the undergraduate experience. If asked, a humanist would have advised the student to think of college work as embarking on an "adventure of ideas"—or, as John Dewey put it, as setting out on a "voyage," a "travelling of the spirit."[9] As it happened, though, most students were not attracted to an intellectual journey of any kind. Instead, they had enrolled in college to secure social advantage, a required credential, or, in a large number of cases, with only the vaguest notion of what they wanted or needed. Moreover, many of these students came to college from high schools that had ill-prepared them to undertake challenging work. Taken together, all of this presented an awkward quandary that humanists found difficult to resolve.

Given these circumstances, what should the humanist do? In 1917, this was the question that Carl Becker put to himself in an irony-laden essay entitled "On Being a Professor." Then on the faculty of the University of Kansas, Becker later moved to Cornell and, over time, would become the most respected historian of his generation. Here, though, he presents himself as a bewildered Arnoldian—that is, as a humanist who belatedly has discovered that his educational aims are in conflict both with the "Zeitgeist" and the facts of the classroom. As a beginning teacher, Becker says, he believed that faculty and students together should think of "four years in college" as "a wonderful adventure in the wide world of the human spirit."[10] After teaching for two decades, however, he had come to accept that very few students joined him in this point of view. There simply could be no denying that most of those under his care, like humankind generally, did not "hunger and thirst after knowledge, anymore than after righteousness." For Becker, this was a troubling recognition. What, he asked, was his duty toward this growing body of students? Did he "best serve...by attending mainly to the great majority or by attending to the saving remnant." The answer to this question, Becker thought, determined whether the professor aimed "to make the university a school of higher education or merely a higher school of education."

But perhaps this question need not be asked. Maybe, Becker admits, the humanist lives too much in the past and wrongly clings to antiquated ideals. For a different approach, why not try to get in step with the new doctrine of "efficiency" recently imported into education from American industry?[11] This quantitative ethic, Becker finds, proclaims that the only questions worth asking about "any educational institution or course of study" are "whether it has a practical value, whether it has a measurable value, and whether its value is equal to its cost." To get "on the right track," therefore, humanists need first to stop bothering about all those "elusive" qualities of intellect and spirit that they, up to now, have believed to be at the heart of a true education. And why not do this? After all, could they any longer provide a compelling (or testable) definition of the wisdom and virtue they thought so important? If not, perhaps the "qualitative arithmetic" taught by the efficiency experts should be welcomed. In applying it, one:

> had only to count, an extremely easy thing to do, and very precise in its results. One had but to count the students in all the universities to determine which was the greatest university, the enrollment in all the course to determine which was the best course. That student was the most liberally educated who obtained the best paying job. The ablest professor was the one who accumulated the most degrees, or printed the most books; while the most efficient was he who taught most hours in the day, or whose name was attended with the longest retinue of varied and noted activities.

Here, then, was a creed that promised an "easy solution" for "all the great problems of education"? To share in this new dispensation, the humanist had only to surrender the fundamental tenet that spiritual and material values should be considered of "a different order altogether" and, in consequence, also cease to insist—as they had long held—that the former can neither be "fostered nor measured by means... appropriate to the latter."

Becker, quite obviously, hopes that his fellow humanists will not be tempted to make any such move. His tone throughout bespeaks utter scorn for a doctrine that proposes to quantify what can only be qualitatively discerned. But nowhere does the essay become a call to battle. Instead, Becker counsels a policy of resignation. In the reigning climate of opinion, he says, conditions favor and support the efficiency experts. And, unhappily, the Zeitgeist "is useless to resist, however little one may enjoy it." So, for now, the humanist should expect that "efficiency" will continue to draw strength from its pledge "to bring education into harmony with the main trend of thought in society at large." Lacking any convictions of its own, Becker laments, the university will always try to mimic the practices that prevail in business, industry, and finance. Moreover, students themselves will prefer to be credited with a numbering of the hours of study they endure rather than be judged for the quality and spirit of their learning. Therefore, given these conditions, humanists must accept the fact that they will appear to be "late survivals" of an outworn tradition. Prudence dictates, then, that they seek a "sheltered corner" in the university and, from there, await the coming of a different time. And what about the spectre of efficiency? Becker's message, in the end, seems to be that this, too, will pass.

Many humanists shared Becker's discomfort with the "qualitative arithmetic" that ruled the university, but I do not suggest that all joined in his resort to quietism. Some, indeed, were quite forceful and direct in their opposition. Of these, Lionel Trilling should be counted among the most articulate. Arnold's biographer, Trilling was one of the most—perhaps *the* most—distinguished humanist of his time (roughly 1945-75). His cultural criticism was wide-ranging, and, running through it, one often finds an insistence on the greater value of the humanities relative to the number-driven social sciences. In fact, in his carefully-wrought essays, one sometimes can sense that he is morally incensed by the power that the social sciences have come to wield both in the academy and society at larger. This indignation perhaps reached a peak in a review of the Kinsey Report that he wrote shortly after this study appeared in 1948. Here Trilling addresses in detail what he sees as the ambitious intent of social science to "speak decisively" about a matter—sexual conduct—that, in its moral bearings, traditionally "has been dealt with by religion, social philosophy and literature."[12]

Trilling's approach to Kinsey's report is that of a cultural critic. Never, that is, does he directly reproach Kinsey for employing flawed statistical methods, making errors, or drawing wrong conclusions—though he leaves no doubt that he believes the report to be defective in all these ways. Instead, he accuses Kinsey of being duplicitous in that his report conceals its true aims from the public. The huge fault of the report, Trilling says, is that it claims to be indifferent "to all questions of morality at the same time that it patently intends a moral effect." Moreover, he adds, all social science shares in this same guilt when it refuses to honor—and make the best of—the subjectivity that necessarily pervades all of its investigative projects. Kinsey, then, stands out only as a very striking case of a much larger failing.

This failure is all the greater, Trilling argues, because it is one that social scientists could easily correct. All they need do, he asserts, is to give up the pretense of "objectivity" and accept that their work, unavoidably, is shot through with moral judgments from beginning to end. They refuse, however, to make any such admission, taking a stance instead based on claims that they—and others—make for the "neutrality" of numbers. Here, particularly, Kinsey serves to illustrate the point. As described by Trilling, Kinsey is a behaviorist to the core. This point of view commits Kinsey to the belief that human sexual experience can be reduced to physical acts of a range and kind observable throughout the natural world. So, having dismissed any semblance of social context or inner sense from his concept of experience, he further narrows the meaning of sex to only those acts that can be counted and numbered. These alone are the "facts," and there is no other admissible evidence of our sexual nature. In this way, Trilling points out, "the sexuality that is measured is taken to be the definition of sexuality itself."[13] From such a standpoint, then, "normality" in sexual behavior becomes entirely a matter of amount and frequency—and this, he observes, leads Kinsey to promote an ethic of "the more the merrier." What empirical finding, Trilling adds, could be more pleasing to the male animal?

In Trilling's estimation, furthermore, Kinsey's work is not only reductive. It also is redundant, and this perhaps is its most disturbing defect. Does the public really need such an extensive quantitative effort to provide it with sexual self-enlightenment? And why should the Rockefeller Foundation and the university have lent this project their authority and favored it with such lavish financial support? These questions, Trilling says, should come to mind when we consider that all the report tells "society as a whole is that there is an almost universal involvement in the sexual life and therefore much variety of conduct." This, after all, is something that could be gathered, at little or no cost, by turning to "any comedy that Aristophanes put on the stage." This, source, however, is one that now is little read and seldom consulted. Sadly, Trilling complains, the same must be said about our literary heritage in its entirety. No one, for instance, could imagine a foundation promoting a return, say, to Lucretius, even though this ancient poet tells us far more about the nature of human sexuality than can be found in the many pages of the Kinsey Report. This, Trilling says, reveals what has become the "established attitude" both among foundations and in universities. In these settings, as well as in the culture at large, quantitative data always trumps literary testimony. So, more than anything else, the Report should be viewed as symptomatic of the kinds of intellectual projects that really count and those which are only marginal. Most especially, the humanists must wake up to this fact and perhaps even be moved to lose their collective temper. Even though civility may suffer, Trilling concludes, such conditions call for resistance rather than restraint, redress rather than retreat.[14]

Here, with Trilling, we have come to the limits of this essay. Taken together, then, what do these case studies tell us? How do they add up? Most especially, what response might the advocates of QL want to make to them? These are questions that I hope we can discuss at Wingspread. For my own part, though, I believe it worth bearing in mind that humanists seem always to have kept a worried eye on quantification. Whatever else they reveal, these case studies do not bespeak indifference. All join Santayana in finding American culture pervaded by a "singular preoccupation with quantity." Often their reaction to this fact has been more emotional than judicious, as much moralistic as analytic. In their view, the cultural workings of quantification have been overbearing and bent on crowding out attention to spirit. To this felt threat, they have pushed back and attempted to hold the quantifiers at bay. In consequence, opposition to quantification has become deeply-seated in the heritage of humanism. Oddly enough, I believe that this adversarial legacy may present an opportunity for QL as it attempts to find allies among and across the liberal arts disciplines. Proponents of QL should consider inviting the humanists to turn first to their own texts as a means of revisiting their stance toward quantification. This, I believe, is much more likely to produce true engagement among humanists than asking that they retrain themselves in sophisticated quantitative methods. Whatever the outcome, humanists are more likely to enter the conversation—and remain involved—if they can begin on familiar ground. At the same time, this also would bring QL into contact with documents and texts about which it so far has had little to say. Here, then, might be found the makings of a genuine conversation.

No one can be sure, of course, that this conversation will be a productive undertaking. Even beginning a cross-disciplinary discussion of this kind will be difficult given the fractured condition of the American educational enterprise. Current circumstances, however, may not be entirely unfavorable to making a start. Albeit not yet in a single voice, many humanists now are calling for a thoroughgoing reconsideration of humanistic practice; and this self-questioning could open new, if still untried, paths through the academic hedgerows. Edward Said, for instance, has urged in a recent series of lectures that his fellow humanists turn from the old "unthinking Arnoldian way" and recognize that "the humanities and humanism are constantly in need of revision, rethinking, and revitalization."[15] Trilling's younger colleague, Said argues that humanists must work to shed the bias toward "withdrawal and exclusion" that has been inherent in their practice and to turn instead, as participatory democratic citizens, to a critical encounter with the "world of contemporary history, politics, and economics." In everyday practice, this means that humanists should attend to an almost limitless array of texts that takes in not just "rarified" literary masterworks but, among others, also includes documents such as policy statements, political pronouncements, and editorial arguments. Said emphasizes that the primary critical concern of the humanists must be with the "language" of these texts, but surely, in taking this direction, the humanist will encounter a language that is laced with quantitative concepts and replete with numbers. When this occurs, one might think that the humanist will be ready to enter into a conversation about how words and numbers mix in our public language in such a way as to act and react upon one another and together join in making meaning. This, anyway, is what I like to believe will happen.

Endnotes

[1] The emphasis is Santayana's own.

[2] On behalf of a Design Team, Lynn Steen writes that QL "clings to specifics, marshaling all relevant aspects of setting and context to reach conclusions." *Mathematics and Democracy: The Case for Quantitative Literacy*, 18.

[3] Laurence Veysey, *The Emergence of the American University*, 338.

[4] Charles Eliot, "What is a Liberal Education," 1876.

[5] Eliot, ibid. [In making this statement, Eliot assumes the existence of an integrated school-college continuum. He also supposes that the American high school eventually will become an educational institution comparable to the German *gymnasium* and the French *lycee*. It is interesting to note how many of the educational policies from this time are still in force even though many of the presuppositions underlying them have never panned out.]

[6] Alan Ryan, *Liberal Anxieties and Liberal Education*, 53-94.

[7] Matthew Arnold, "Numbers: Or, The Majority and the Remnant," in *Discourses in America*, 5.

[8] Henry James, *The American Scene*, 45-6.

[9] John Dewey, "A College Course: What Should I Expect from It?" *Collected Works, Volume 3, 1889-1892*, 52.

[10] The leading advocates for "efficiency" were known as "educationists" and most held positions in major schools of education. Their agenda promoted displacement of disciplinary frameworks in favor of a curriculum organized around a quantification of common activities in categories of "everyday life, e.g., such as health, family, and leisure." This assault on the disciplines led to an estrangement of liberal arts faculty from schools of education that persists to this day. For an extended discussion of this matter see Robert Orrill and Linn Shapiro, "From Bold Beginnings to an Uncertain Future," *American Historical Review*, (June 2005), 727-51.

[11] Carl Becker, "On Being a Professor," in *Detachment and the Writing of History.*

[12] Lionel Trilling, "The Kinsey Report," in *The Liberal Imagination*, 216-34.

[13] In a like manner, psychometricians define intelligence as those limited aspects of "intelligence" that their instruments enable them to measure

[14] A personal note. I have been on the receiving end of Trilling's anger and know at first hand that his own renowned civility, though admirable, also had its limits.

[15] Edward Said, *Humanism and Democratic Criticism*, (2004), pp. 31-56. These lectures were delivered just prior to Said's untimely death.

Arguing with Numbers: Teaching Quantitative Reasoning through Argument and Writing

Neil Lutsky
*Carleton College**

> *Numbers [are] the principal language of public argument*
> — "More or Less," BBC Radio Programme (2007)

This chapter argues for numbers and for an approach to teaching quantitative reasoning that involves secondary and post-secondary teachers representing diverse subject matters and disciplines. My arguments are organized around the following propositions:

(i) *Strengthening students' quantitative reasoning is an imperative of contemporary general education.* This critical need is insufficiently addressed across secondary and post-secondary curricula. One reason is that current justifications for quantitative literacy across the curriculum do not appear relevant to what teachers are charged with doing or believe themselves prepared to do in their classes. That leads to proposition (ii).

(ii) *A fitting context for quantitative reasoning is argumentation, the construction, communication, and evaluation of arguments.* I argue quantitative

---

* Neil Lutsky is William R. Kenan, Jr. Professor of Psychology at Carleton College in Northfield, MN. He is the principal investigator on a grant from the Department of Education FIPSE program funding Carleton's Quirk (Quantitative Reasoning, Inquiry, and Knowledge) initiative. As part of this project, he has developed a new course, Measured Thinking: Reasoning with Numbers about World Events, Health, Science, and Social Issues, to introduce first year students to quantitative reasoning and to involve those students in service learning projects that call upon their quantitative expertise. Lutsky earned his B.S. in Economics from Penn's Wharton School and his Ph.D. degree in Social Psychology from Harvard University. He is a past president of the Society for the Teaching of Psychology, a blue ribbon winner for jams at the Minnesota State Fair, and an avid if slow road bicyclist. *E-mail*: nlutsky@carleton.edu.

reasoning is potentially relevant to a wide variety of claims individuals seek to advance in public discourse and will present evidence from a particular sample of arguments in college students' written work in partial support of that assertion. Quantitative reasoning can help students as they construct and evaluate arguments. This is because quantitative reasoning can contribute to the framing, articulation, testing, principled presentation, and public analysis of arguments. But what quantitative reasoning skills are especially useful for the purposes of constructing, communicating, and evaluating arguments? That leads to proposition (iii).

(iii) *The quantitative reasoning habits students need to learn are primarily simple and non-technical.* I seek to elaborate this point by listing 10 quantitative reasoning questions that may help students interrogate arguments or prepare arguments for interrogation. But in what contexts might teachers advance quantitative reasoning skills pegged to basic concerns? That leads to proposition (iv).

(iv) *The teaching of quantitative reasoning across the curriculum might not only model itself on the teaching of writing across the curriculum; it might be intertwined with teaching writing.* I will identify suggestions for teaching students to argue with numbers in their writing. These are based on the outcomes of research my colleagues and I have conducted on student uses, misuses, and missed uses of quantitative reasoning in written work and on resources available to teachers seeking to integrate the teaching of writing and of quantitative reasoning.

Quantitative Literacy in General Education

Why does quantitative literacy merit keen attention in the agenda of secondary and post-secondary education? Lynn Steen and his associates (1997, 2001, 2004) have answered this question in compelling fashion by highlighting how pervasive quantitative information is in contemporary life. Numbers are a staple of accounts of world events (Paulos, 1995), environmental trends and challenges (e.g., Gore, 2006), public policy (e.g., Best, 2001, 2004), financial matters and investing (e.g., Taleb, 2004), consumer choices and advertising (e.g., Seelye, 2006), medical news and health decision-making (e.g., Gigerenzer, 2002), educational assessments (e.g. American Institutes for Research, 2006), economic and technological developments (e.g., Friedman, 2005; Committee on Prospering in the Global Economy of the 21st Century, 2005), science news (e.g., Goldacre, 2005), and everyday issues (e.g., Levitt & Dubner, 2005). As Steen has stated, "The world of the twenty-first century is a world awash in numbers" (1997, p. 1).

As educators we need to draw attention to *why* numbers are so widely used in modern life (e.g., Cohen, 2005; Porter, 1995). We need to show others that numbers can contribute to precision in our thinking, facilitate the public discussion and evaluation of claims, help us grasp the attributes of large and complex phenomena, organize vast domains of information, and help us discover patterns of relationships not readily available to human perception. In sum, numbers are not only important because they are pervasive; they are pervasive because they are important. It is because numbers have both the power to influence and the power to inform that we need to educate citizens to attend to numbers, to understand them, and to think thoughtfully and critically about them.

Recent discussions of the goals of higher education acknowledge the growing significance of quantitative literacy, and credit for that rests, at least in part, with advocates such as Best (e.g., 2004), Madison and Steen (2003), Paulos (1988), Schield (2005), Steen (1997, 2001, 2004), and others. Derek Bok (2006), for example, is promoting a list of broad aims for contemporary undergraduate education, including strengthening communication skills, critical thinking, moral reasoning, responsible citizenship, appreciations of diversity, involvement in a global society, breadth of knowledge, and preparations for work. In the context of his treatment of critical thinking, he notes, "certain basic quantitative methods seem applicable to a wide enough range of situations to be valuable for almost all students" (2006, p. 69). (I would add, in keeping with the arguments of those aforementioned advocates, that quantitative literacy could be seen as equally essential to other educational purposes Bok identifies, such as appreciating diversity, living in a more global society, and preparing for work.) Similarly, a recent report by the Association of American Colleges and Universities (2005), *Liberal Education Outcomes*, suggests that there is "a remarkable consensus on a few key outcomes that all students, regardless of major or academic background, should achieve during undergraduate study" (p. 2). That report specifies quantitative literacy as one of those outcomes (see also the 2007 Association of American of Colleges and Universities report, *College Learning for the New Global Century*). Finally, if the reader prefers a more succinct curricular directive, he or she could do no better than Princeton philosopher K. Anthony Appiah's general education recommendation to contemporary students under the heading: "Learn Statistics. Go Abroad" (Appiah, 2005).

One feature common to current curricular discussions is support for a quantitative literacy across the curriculum approach. This has long been advocated in the quantitative literacy literature (e.g., Orrill, 1997, p. xiii) and has been reiterated in broad treatments of curricular priorities. Bok (2006), for example, suggests that:

...numeracy is not something mastered in a single course. The ability to apply quantitative methods to real-world problems requires a faculty and an insight and intuition that can be developed only through repeated practice. Thus quantitative material needs to permeate the curriculum. (p. 134)

This call for quantitative literacy to be taught across the general education curriculum, as well as across all levels of education (Conference Board of the Mathematical Sciences, 2001), resonates with what educators and psychologists know about conditions that facilitate generalized learning. For example, Halpern and Hakel (2003) conclude that teaching for the transfer (generalization) and long-term retention of knowledge requires learners "to generate responses, with minimal cues, repeatedly over time with varied applications so that recall becomes fluent and is more likely to occur across difference contexts and content domains" (p. 38).

But how can quantitative literacy be taught for the purposes of general education? One response to this is to teach quantitative literacy in mathematics and (a) hope that students have reinforcing encounters with quantitative thinking in other courses, or (b) orient the quantitative mathematics courses themselves to be more broadly problem-based (e.g., Nolan & Speed, 1999). Another response is to teach quantitative literacy in other disciplines that employ quantitative analysis as an investigative tool, such as the social sciences, and to relieve mathematics of the sole or even primary educational responsibility for quantitative literacy. This chapter argues for a third way, one that has the potential to broaden the uses to which quantitative reasoning is put and the places in the curriculum it is taught.

The model it emulates is writing across the curriculum. As David Bressoud wrote in the forward to *Achieving Quantitative Literacy* (Steen, 2004), "Quantitative literacy does not need to be taught only by mathematicians any more than effective writing needs to be taught only by English professors" (p. ix). But however compelling it might be on educational grounds to teach quantitative literacy across the curriculum and however appropriate it might be to do so in meaningful, distributed contexts, there are reasons why it has proven much more difficult to forge quantitative literacy across the curriculum initiatives than writing across the curriculum ones. Writing is a means of expression common to most disciplines, whereas quantitative literacy appears relevant to courses in the social and natural sciences but, with minor exceptions, not elsewhere. Moreover, secondary and post-secondary instructors are more likely to be confident in their abilities to teach writing than quantitative analysis, even if only at a basic level. So key challenges remain: why should teachers in a variety of subject matters believe quantitative literacy is relevant to what they do and, moreover, why should they believe they possess the ability and background to help students strengthen quantitative reasoning habits of mind? Perhaps these challenges can be met if we reconsider the conventional contextual framing of quantitative literacy.

Quantitative Reasoning in the Context of Argument

The primary thesis of this chapter is that quantitative literacy can be usefully situated in the context of argument, in the presentation of statements supporting claims. In this sense, arguments are not only reasons to take one position or another on a contentious issue but address explicit and even implicit claims about the nature of a phenomenon or the importance of a topic (see, e.g., Fulkerson, 1996; Ramage, Bean, & Johnson, 2007). Teaching students how to identify and find the constituent elements of an argument, how to organize arguments systematically, what kinds of statements support particular arguments effectively, how to present arguments clearly and meaningfully to an audience, how to address their own arguments reflectively, and how to evaluate others' arguments *are* fundamental to education at all levels and in almost all disciplines.

What can quantitative information do for arguments? Among other things, quantitative information may be used to help articulate or clarify an argument, frame or draw attention to an argument, make a descriptive argument, or support, qualify, or evaluate an argument. Quantitative analysis may also influence how arguments are marshaled and how exchanges of arguments are conducted. As Robert Abelson (1995) wrote, "the purpose of statistics is to organize a useful argument from quantitative evidence, using a form of principled rhetoric" (1995, p. xiii). Moreover, such arguments are open to knowledgeable evaluation. According to Theodore Porter (1995), "In practice, objectivity and factuality rarely mean self-evident truth. Instead, they imply openness to possible refutation by other experts" (p. 214). This is one of the signal virtues of quantitative analysis; it contributes to open tests of ideas that can be reported in argument and evaluated by others.

Quantitative reasoning has been linked to argumentation previously, but in the existing literature primarily so with regards to how quantitative results are interpreted (although students also commonly face the challenge of taking word problems and figuring out what statistical procedures might be needed to answer them). There is a wonderful Edward Koren cartoon from *The New Yorker* (December 9, 1974) showing the personified numbers 9, 6, 2, 1, 8, and 4 seated on chairs on stage being introduced by a man at the podium who quips, "Tonight, we're going to let the statistics speak for themselves." Of course, we all know that the numbers do not speak for themselves; someone advocates a case for the sense the numbers might make. To be sure, that is a significant domain of quantitative reasoning, of arguments about the meaning of numbers that are used in arguments with numbers. The Conference Board of the Mathematical Sciences (2001), for example, repeatedly cites interpretation, "relating the results of data analysis back to original questions and stating conclusions" (p. 87), as a basic task elementary, middle school, and high school teachers of statistics should address. But interpreting the meaning of numbers represents only one way in which we argue with numbers, one in which the numbers themselves are the focus of attention rather than the larger arguments of which they are a part.

What a broader approach to examining the relationship between quantitative reasoning and argumentation might yield became clearer to me and my colleagues at Carleton College as we undertook activities associated with our Quantitative Inquiry, Reasoning, and Knowledge (Quirk) initiative. Two years ago eight faculty and academic support staff met to read and discuss papers submitted as part of student writing portfolios required to meet the College's writing requirement. We wanted to learn whether and how students used quantitative reasoning in written arguments to help us orient workshops for faculty and academic staff. After this informal inquiry, we began developing a more systematic approach to evaluating student papers for quantitative reasoning using a coding rubric we have since been refining (see Quirk Rubric for the Assessment of Quantitative Reasoning in Student Writing, 2007).

What became clear as we developed the rubric was that there were at least two general ways in which students used quantitative reasoning in written argumentation: peripherally and centrally. Peripheral uses cite numbers to provide details, enrich descriptions, present background, or establish frames of reference. Jane Miller (2004), in *The Chicago Guide to Writing about Numbers*, captured the spirit of peripheral applications of quantitative information when she advised her reader, "Even for works that are not inherently quantitative, one or two numeric facts can help convey the importance or context of your topic" (p. 1). An example of a peripheral use of quantitative information is given in a psychology paper that is centrally concerned with identifying possible psychogenic pain mechanisms but peripherally discusses the incidence of psychogenic pain in an introductory paragraph. Central uses of numbers address a *primary* question, issue, or theme in a paper. An example of a central use of quantitative information is given in a paper for an economics course evaluating the need for quotas on textile and apparel imports from China.

We have been using the rubric to code randomly drawn student papers from the portfolios as "potentially employing quantitative information peripherally" or as "potentially employing quantitative information centrally" or as "not at all or incidentally potentially involving quantitative information" (see Lutsky & Tassava, in preparation, for details). Over two studies (Lutsky, 2006, Lutsky & Tassava, in preparation), we found that roughly two thirds of all papers assessed, representing a sample of papers from courses across the curriculum, were judged as potentially involving quantitative information. Approximately a third of the entire sample of papers potentially involved quantitative information in a peripheral role and a third potentially involved quantitative information in a central role. (Quantitative reasoning was judged as irrelevant to the remaining third of papers.) The peripheral set included papers from across the curriculum; papers from the social and natural sciences dominated the central set. In addition, we judged that two thirds of the papers for which quantitative information was potentially centrally relevant in fact used quantitative reasoning. However, only 12% of the papers for which quantitative information was potentially peripherally relevant used quantitative reasoning.

What do we take these findings as suggesting? First, we should acknowledge that the sample of papers we considered reflects certain limiting conditions (e.g., selection by students to meet the criteria for portfolio inclusion). Moreover, the relevance of quantitative reasoning was judged by two evaluators sensitive to potential uses of quantitative information. Nonetheless, we would advance two tentative observations: (a) quantitative information is potentially relevant to arguments posed in papers from across the curriculum, and (b) quantitative reasoning is strikingly underutilized for peripheral purposes in papers from across the curriculum. The latter is a key finding: *quantitative reasoning could be employed for peripheral argumentation in writing across the curriculum but currently that is not happening.*

Viewing quantitative reasoning through the lens of argumentation raises new challenges for educators. How can we demonstrate to students when quantitative information may be useful in framing or evaluating arguments? How can we train students to find or generate the quantitative information they might begin to seek? At Carleton we have found it useful to work with college librarians to help instruct students on locating relevant data, evaluating data sources, and checking quantitative information. In other words, quantitative literacy in this context has led to a concern for information literacy.

We have also pursued means of teaching students how quantitative evidence might be presented effectively. For example, Fulkerson (1996) suggested readers would evaluate the substantiation for claims in terms of four criteria, which he labeled using the acronym STAR. The first is Sufficiency, whether there is enough evidence provided. The second is Typicality, whether the evidence presented is representative. The third is Accuracy, whether the data are true. And the fourth is Relevance, whether the evidence is centrally connected to the claim. Quantitative information can be evaluated *as evidence* in light of these criteria and can also provide the grounds for reasoning about the adequacy of substantiations offered for a claim.

In sum, what I have argued above is that a fitting context for quantitative reasoning is argument. As Max Frankel, the Pulitzer Prize winning former editor of *The New York Times* suggested, "Deploying numbers skillfully is as important to communication as deploying verbs" (1995, p. 24). Offering, evaluating, and discussing arguments are activities that are common to a wide range of subject matters. As teachers endeavor to help students think about what makes arguments clear and effective, and how to construct sound and principled arguments, teachers may, if sufficiently trained, prompted, and informed, come to recognize the important roles that quantitative reasoning may play in argumentation. What we have seen is that quantitative reasoning is potentially relevant in both peripheral and central ways to the presentation of arguments, and that potential peripheral uses of quantitative reasoning are both relevant across the curriculum and sorely lacking. That suggests those of us who promote quantitative reasoning across the curriculum have an opportunity to introduce quantitative issues to our colleagues in a simpler, more accessible way than we have previously emphasized.

Quantitative Reasoning Made Simple and Then More Complicated

What is it that we want to educate students to do quantitatively? Taking the construction and evaluation of arguments as a primary concern and remaining attentive to peripheral uses of quantitative information may lead to a recon-sideration and simplification of standard quantitative literacy agendas (e.g., Conference Board of the Mathematical Sciences, 2001, pp. 43-44; Steen, 2001, pp. 15-17), at least at the outset of quantitative education. I am not claiming the changes would be radical, nor do I believe they should be, but I do hope the ex-amples of quantitative opportunities and misinterpretations we highlight will become more accessible, relevant, and meaningful to teachers and students when they first encounter quantitative reasoning.

Consider an example of the kind of shortcoming we often tout, recently labeled by Howard Wainer (2007) as "the most dangerous equation" because ignorance of the equation has led to important misunderstandings of quantitative evidence. This is the equation for the standard deviation of the sampling distribution of the mean (i.e., the standard error). Not understanding that variation is likely to be larger when sample sizes are smaller has led,

Wainer shows, to misattributions of the meaning of extreme outcomes derived from small samples. Essentially, statistical artifacts are taken as meaningful. Insensitivity to the relationship between sample size and variability is common in human cognition, as the well-known work of psychologists Tversky and Kahneman (1974) has documented.

I wish, as Wainer does, that these statistical effects were more widely appreciated. But this is not the kind of understanding that is readily accessible to quantitative novices, who may have little sense of what a standard deviation is or what the sampling distribution of the mean is. I need to make clear that in citing this example, I mean no criticism of Wainer, who, after all, was writing for readers of *American Scientist*. My point is that moderately complex examples of unsound statistical reasoning may not encourage educators to promote quantitative reasoning. Rather, what I think we need are simple examples of how quantitative information may strengthen peripheral and central arguments and straightforward questions that can be asked of quantitative claims.

My own attempt to identify a general education agenda for quantitative reasoning represents a response to the following prompt: *What questions would I most want my students spontaneously posing when they encounter opportunities for quantitative argument or existing quantitative arguments?* I have constructed a list of 10 such questions, which I call QR Questions at the Ready (Lutsky, in preparation). These are rooted in the quantitative literacy literature (e.g., Best, 2001, 2004; Goldacre, 2005; Niederman & Boyum, 2003; Paulos, 1988; Steen, 1997, 2001, 2004), my experiences developing and teaching a seminar for first year students at Carleton (Measured Thinking: Reasoning with Numbers about World Events, Health, Science, and Social Issues), and the readings and discussions my colleagues at Carleton and I have had on students' uses of quantitative reasoning, especially as shown in their writing.

What I have tried to do in the list is to state the 10 framing questions in as general a way as possible. Each question subsumes more specific questions, such as those shown, and many of specific questions point to more technical quantitative procedures and issues. I do not take the list to be comprehensive or the best possible list of 10 questions relevant to reasoning about quantitative claims, but I do hope it will stimulate thinking about how we might make quantitative reasoning more accessible to a broad audience in education and beyond.

Here is the list of ten QR "Questions at the Ready":

1. *What do the numbers show?* How can numerical information be used to establish the context or significance of a topic? What is the magnitude of a phenomenon? How can numbers help describe something more precisely?

Is there numerical evidence to support a claim? What are the exact figures? What do cited numbers mean?

2. *How typical is that?* Is the example or anecdotal evidence representative? What is the central tendency? How typical is the central tendency of the scores as a whole or of the scores in subgroups? What is the base rate? What are the odds of that?

3. *Compared to what?* What is the implicit or explicit frame of reference? What is the unit of measurement? Per what? What is the order of magnitude? What defines the Y-axis?

4. *Are findings those of a single study or source or of multiple studies or sources?* What is the source of the numbers? How reliable is it? Has the source been peer-reviewed? Who is sponsoring the research? How plausible is a claimed outcome in light of back of the envelope calculations? Has the finding been replicated? Is there a literature on the finding? Are there converging conclusions from multiple sources? Can the results of a literature be summarized quantitatively? What do the results of relevant meta-analyses indicate?

5. *How were the main characteristics measured?* How were key variables operationalized? What evidence is there that the measurement procedures were reliable, valid, and otherwise sound ones for the purposes of the study? What meaning and degree of precision does the measurement procedure justify?

6. *Who or what was studied?* What domain is being studied? Who or what was sampled from this domain? How was that sample constituted? Was it random? How equivalent are any samples that are being compared?

7. *Is the outcome of a study anything more than noise or chance?* Is the outcome unlikely to have come about by chance (i.e., statistically significant)?

8. *How large is the result of a study?* How substantial is the result? How practically important is it? What is the effect size?

9. *What was the design of the study?* To what extent does the design support causal inferences? Is the design that of a true experiment? Was an experiment double blind?

10. *What else might be influencing the findings?* What other variables might be affecting the findings? Were those assessed or otherwise controlled for in the research design? What do not we know, and how can we acknowledge uncertainties?

Again, I would not claim that the list is sufficient or that it gracefully parses quantitative reasoning at its joints. Pragmatically and logically the first question is most fundamental. We need to teach students the value of thinking in terms of numbers. We need to encourage them to seek relevant numbers, both when they argue and when they evaluate the arguments of others. That is the foundational habit of mind upon which more sophisticated and technical structures of quantitative reasoning can be built.

Writing as a Locus for Teaching Quantitative Reasoning

The teaching of writing provides an inviting opportunity for addressing quantitative reasoning because "argument pervades writing" (Fulkerson, 1996, p. 2). Key values in writing, such as precision in word selection, clarity of expression, persuasiveness, soundness of supporting scholarship and evidence, logical organization, and appeal to readers may be facilitated by quantitatively informed arguments. Writing also involves active learning as students use and think about numbers. Moreover, writing assignments typically give students time to prepare—research, write, and revise—their work and teachers the time to create the educational scaffolding to strengthen writing with numbers.

One essential way teachers can facilitate quantitative reasoning is to give students writing assignments that invite or require quantitative reasoning. Assignments that call for quantitative analysis centrally may be common in the social and natural sciences or in applied statistics courses. Examples of such assignments from across the curriculum are available at the web site of the Science Education Resource Center (Quantitative Writing, 2007). Deann Leoni (2005) has also developed excellent assignments that integrate mathematics and English and get high school students writing with and about numbers.

A major implication of the finding reported earlier on potential peripheral uses of quantitative information is that more could be done to encourage students to cite relevant numbers to frame and introduce topics. That has led us to promote a simple suggestion to faculty at Carleton. *It is to ask students in writing assignments to use numbers to set an example or case study of primary interest in a paper in its wider context.* You may recognize that this is an instantiation of the second of those QR Questions at the Ready: How typical or representative is this? The question has the virtues of directing students to think in terms of numbers and of requiring them to learn how to find (and possibly evaluate) numbers. Typicality of information may also help a writer and his or her reader think about the extent to which and the ways in which the characteristics of the example should be generalized.

Most of the literature on writing and quantitative reasoning offers suggestions for effective ways to write about numbers. A particularly helpful resource for teachers and students in this regard is *The Chicago Guide to Writing About Numbers* (Miller, 2004). Miller identifies principles for expressing numbers in writing, including seven basic ones. These are: (1) establish the context, (2) choose effective examples and analogies, (3) use an appropriate vocabulary, (4) decide where to present numbers, (5) report and interpret numbers in text, (6) specify the size and direction of associations, and (7) summarize overall patterns. Miller also provides specific writing examples to illustrate poor, better, and best efforts to meet these writing goals.

Other authors have particular concerns about how numbers are represented in words. MacNeal (1994), in *Mathsemantics: Making Numbers Talk Sense*, decries the confusion of events with people. Gigerenzer (2002) discusses how representing risks in terms of "natural frequencies" rather than probabilities enhances public understanding. Niederman and Boyum (2003) and Paulos (1988) discuss means of representing units of measurement or large numbers to make them more accessible to readers.

At Carleton we have identified several recurring problems in student writing with numbers. The first, called the *weasel word problem*, highlights overuse of the terms "many," "often," "some," and others of that ilk in the place of either appropriate caution or numbers. Shafer (2005) neatly skewered a front-page article in *The New York Times* (Story, 2005) suffering from the same problem. A second concern, the *staples problem*, refers to papers in which quantitative information in the form of tables and figures is stapled onto a paper but not interpreted in the text (see also Miller's principle 5). A third shortcoming, the *comparison problem*, indicates instances in which students cite numbers but do not provide frames of reference that might make those numbers meaningful (see also Question 3 of the 10 QR Questions at the Ready). Finally, we have also noted a *terminology variability problem* in the uses of key quantitative terms. Different academic disciplines socialize students to give words such as "experiment" (see Question 9 of 10 QR Questions) more or less restricted meanings.

Other challenges face the teacher attempting to promote student writing using numbers. One, common to writing, is taking the role of the potential reader. How much information and what form of information will be meaningful to readers? One way I have tried to respond to this question in my first year seminar is to bring student writers face to face with readers. I have done this in service learning projects in which teams of students take data collected by community organizations (e.g., the regional Girl Scouts council, a local bike tour) and prepare reports based on the data. I have had the leaders of the community groups come to class to discuss with students what would make the reports most useful to their organizations. Another important form of this same problem is addressing the reasonable questions of an informed reader. What questions are readers likely to raise about the quantitative claims (findings) presented in a paper? How can these be anticipated and handled in a written report? Finally, a difficult challenge for all of us who use numbers in writing is stating claims with degrees of certainty appropriate to the state of the evidence. As Robert Kuhn has noted, "the cognitive skill to distinguish among hope, faith, possibility, probability, and certitude are potent weapons in anyone's political survival kit and can be applied in all areas of life and society" (2003, p. 388).

Coda

In a study at Harvard University, Richard Light (2001) asked undergraduate students to identify the characteristics of "faculty who make a difference." What is it that those faculty do as educators that, according to student self-reports, has a profound impact? Two of the nine attributes students listed were these: teaching precision in the use of language, and teaching the use of evidence. The arguments presented in this chapter suggest the two are not unrelated to each other and are both potentially intertwined with applications of quantitative reasoning. Can recognizing that transform how teachers in secondary and post-secondary education address quantitative reasoning? That, I believe, is an argument worth testing.

Acknowledgements. The author gratefully acknowledges suggestions for this paper from Nathan Grawe and Carol Rutz, Carleton College, and two reviewers. Ideas and findings presented in this chapter were developed in collaborations that have been part of Carleton College's Quantitative Inquiry, Reasoning, and Knowledge (Quirk) initiative. The author is deeply indebted to colleagues in Quirk for their stimulating insights and ongoing dedication. Quirk is supported by a grant from the Fund for the Improvement of Post-Secondary Education, U. S. Department of Education (www.ed.gov/FIPSE). Additional information on Carleton's Quirk initiative is available at serc.carleton.edu/quirk.

References

Abelson, R. P. (1995). *Statistics as principled argument.* Hillsdale, NJ: Lawrence Erlbaum Press.

American Institutes for Research. (2006). The literacy of America's college students. www.air.org/news/default.aspx#pew

Appiah, K. A. (2005). Learn statistics. Go abroad. www.slate.com/id/2130328/

Association of American of Colleges and Universities. (2005). *Liberal education outcomes*. www.aacu.org/advocacy/pdfs/LEAP_Report_FINAL.pdf

Association of American of Colleges and Universities. (2007). *College learning for the new global century*. www.aacu.org/advocacy/leap/exec_summary.cfm

Best, J. (2001). *Damned lies and statistics*. Berkeley, CA: University of California Press.

Best, J. (2004). *More damned lies and statistics*. Berkeley, CA: University of California Press.

Bok, D. (2006). *Our underachieving colleges.* Princeton, NJ: Princeton University Press.

Bressoud, D. M. (2004). Foreword. In L. A. Steen (Ed.), *Achieving quantitative literacy* (pp. ix). Washington, DC: Mathematical Association of America.

Cohen, I. B. (2005). *The triumph of numbers: How counting shaped modern life.* New York, NY: Norton.

Committee on Prospering in the Global Economy of the 21st Century (2005). *Rising above the gathering storm: Energizing and employing America for a brighter economic future.* books.nap.edu/catalog/11463.html

Conference Board of the Mathematical Sciences. (2001). *The mathematical education of teachers*. Providence, RI and Washington DC: American Mathematical Society and Mathematical Association of America.

Frankel, M. (1995, March 5). Innumeracy. *The New York Times Magazine, 144,* 24.

Friedman, T. L. (2005). *The world is flat: A brief history of the twenty-first century.* New York, NY: Farrar, Straus, and Giroux.

Fulkerson, R. (1996). *Teaching the argument in writing.* Urbana, IL: National Council of Teachers of English.

Gigerenzer, G. (2002). *Calculated risks: How to know when numbers deceive you.* New York, NY: Simon & Schuster.

Goldacre, B. (2005, September 8). Don't dumb me down. *The Guardian.* www.guardian.co.uk/life/badscience/story/0,12980,1564369,00.html

Gore, A. (2006). *An inconvenient truth: The planetary emergency of global warming and what we can do about it.* New York, NY: Rodale.

Halpern, D. F., & Hakel, M. D. (2003). Applying the science of learning to the university and beyond. *Change*, July/August, 36–41.

Kuhn, R. L. (2003). Science as democratizer. *American Scientist, 91,* 388.

Leoni, D. (2005). Algebra the write way. Retrieved April 7, 2007, from math.dartmouth. edu/~matc/eBookshelf/literature/AWW.phtml

Levitt, S. D., & Dubner, S. J. (2005). *Freakonomics: A rogue economist explores the hidden side of everything.* New York, NY: William Morrow.

Light, R. J. (2001). *Making the most of college: Students speak their minds*. Cambridge, MA: Harvard University Press.

Lutsky, N. (2006). Quirks of rhetoric: A quantitative analysis of quantitative reasoning in student writing. *Proceedings of the Joint Statistical Meetings, 2006.* Alexandria, VA; American Statistical Association.

Lutsky, N. (2007). *QR questions at the ready.* Manuscript in preparation.

Lutsky, N., & Tassava, C. (2007). *A method for the quantitative assessment of quantitative reasoning in student writing.* Manuscript in preparation.

MacNeal, E. (1994). *Mathsemantics: Making numbers talk sense.* New York, NY: Penguin Books.

Madison, B. L., & Steen, L. A. (Eds.) (2003). *Quantitative literacy: Why numeracy matters for schools and colleges.* Princeton, NJ: The National Council on Education and the Disciplines.

Miller, J. E. (2004). *The Chicago guide to writing about numbers.* Chicago, IL: University of Chicago Press.

More or Less, British Broadcasting Corporation radio programme. Retrieved April 27, 2007, from news.bbc.co.uk/2/hi/programmes/more_or_less/1628489.stm

Niederman, D., & Boyum, D. (2003). *What the numbers say: A field guide to mastering our numerical world.* New York, NY: Broadway Books.

Nolan, D., & Speed, T. P. (1999). Teaching statistics theory through applications. *American Statistician, 53,* 370–375.

Orrill, R. (1997). Foreword. In L. A. Steen (Ed.), *Why numbers count: Quantitative literacy for tomorrow's America* (pp. xi–xiv). New York, NY: College Entrance Examination Board.

Paulos, J. A. (1988). *Innumeracy: Mathematical illiteracy and its consequences.* New York, NY: Hill and Wang.

Paulos, J. A. (1995). *A mathematician reads the newspaper.* New York, NY: Anchor Books.

Porter, T. (1995). *Trust in numbers: The pursuit of objectivity in science and public life.* Princeton, NJ: Princeton University Press.

Quantitative writing. Retrieved April 30, 2007, from serc.carleton.edu/sp/carl_ltc/quantitative_writing/index.html

Quirk rubric for the assessment of quantitative reasoning in student writing. Retrieved May 1, 2007, from apps.carleton.edu/collab/quirk/resources/Rubric/

Ramage, J. D., Bean, J. C., & Johnson, J. (2007). *Writing arguments: A rhetoric with readings.* New York, NY: Pearson.

Schield, M. (2005). *Statistical literacy: Seeing the story behind the statistics.* US: Instant Publisher.

Seelye, K. Q. (2006, February 10). Lurid numbers on glossy pages! (Magazines exploit what sells). *New York Times,* p. A1.

Shafer, J. (2005, September 20). Weasel-words rip my flesh! *Slate.* slate.msn.com/id/2126636/

Shulman, L. S. (2004). *Teaching as community property: Essays on higher education.* San Francisco, CA: Jossey-Bass.

Steen, L. A. (Ed.) (1997). *Why numbers count: Quantitative literacy for tomorrow's America.* New York, NY: College Entrance Examination Board.

Steen, L. A. (Ed.) (2001). *Mathematics and democracy.* Princeton, NJ: National Council on Education and the Disciplines.

Steen, L. A. (2004). *Achieving quantitative literacy.* Washington, DC: The Mathematical Association of America.

Story, L. (2005, September 20). Many women at elite colleges set career path to motherhood. *New York Times*, p. 1. www.nytimes.com/2005/09/20/national/20women.html?ex=1284868800&en=6a8e0c413c09c249&ei=5090&partner=rssuserl and&emc=rss

Taleb, N. N. (2004). *Fooled by randomness: The hidden role of chance in markets and life, 2nd Edition.* New York, NY: Random House.

Tversky, A., & Kahneman, D. (1974). Judgment under uncertainty: Heuristics and biases. *Science, 185,* 1124–1131.

Wainer, H. (2007). The most dangerous equation. *American Scientist, 95,* 249–256.

Fractions and Units in Everyday Life

Alan Tucker

*State University of New York-Stony Brook**

Fractions, in the form of percentages and rates, are pervasive in the workplace and in decision-making in one's personal life. However, it is in the transition from whole number arithmetic to fractions that too many students fall off the ladder of mathematical learning. They continue their education and become adults without ever understanding fractions.

Consider the following question on the TIMSS 8th grade test:

Find the approximate value, to the closest integer, of the sum: $19/20$ $+ 23/25$.

Possible answers were a) 1, b) 2, c) 42, d) 45. (Answer: b) The majority of U.S. students chose c) or d). These students did not think of a fraction as a number. When asked to add two fractions and get an integer answer, they added the numerators or the denominators of the two fractions. The only numbers that they knew about were counting numbers (whole numbers). A fraction to them was some combination of two whole numbers. To be fair, fractions are a sophisticated mathematical concept compared to whole numbers.

The critical concept underlying fractions is units. By a unit, we mean a standard reference for measurement or counting. Units range from simple standards like inches and cents to more subtle standards such as the amount

---
* Alan Tucker is S.U.N.Y. Distinguished Teaching Professor at the State University of New York-Stony Brook in the Department of Applied Mathematics and Statistics. He obtained his PhD in Mathematics from Stanford University in 1969 and has been at Stony Brook since 1970. His research specialty is combinatorial mathematics. He is the author of three textbooks and 40 research publications. He has been first vice-president of the Mathematical Association of America (MAA), chair of its education council and recipient of the MAA's national award for distinguished university teaching of mathematics. He was the lead author of *The Mathematical Education of Teachers* (CBMS, 2001) and *Assessing Calculus Reform Efforts* (MAA, 1995). Currently, he directs the MAA project Preparing Mathematicians to Educate Teachers funded by grants from NSF and Texas Instruments. *E-mail*: atucker@notes.cc.sunysb.edu.

of sugar—say, 2/3rds of a cup of sugar—required in a recipe for a batch of brownies. Units also turn out to be the key to understanding multi-step, whole-number word problems. Being able to solve such word problems, along with using fractions, are the mathematical knowledge that a Business Roundtable task force (Schaar, 2005) has identified as essential for assembly line workers now employed in technologically oriented companies. Moreover, understanding fractions in the framework presented here is a critical foundation for quantitative reasoning in the modern world.

Whole number arithmetic was once all the mathematics that most people used in their jobs. Today, whole number arithmetic is performed in the workplace by machines for the sake of record keeping as well as accuracy. Employees no longer do arithmetic calculations themselves. Whole number arithmetic is still needed for simple mental calculations throughout daily life, but increasingly *its primary importance is as the mathematical foundation for future mathematical learning.*

Fractions have come to have a major role in the workplace. Whether on production lines or managers' desks, many of the numbers one encounters in business today are percents and rates—error rate, interest rate, employment rate, productivity level, etc. Thus all citizens today need to know how to use and interpret fractions. International comparisons like TIMSS reveal that too many U.S. students, in comparison to students in other countries, have trouble making the transition from whole number arithmetic to fractions. Efforts are underway to reorganize mathematics instruction in early grades to give greater attention to preparing students for fractions.

While instruction about fractions for college students, as part of a quantitative literacy curriculum, will obviously be different from K–8 instruction about fractions, a natural starting point for the former instruction is the extensive research about learning fractions in grades K–8 that has been undertaken by mathematics educators as well as several mathematicians. This essay attempts to summarize some of this research, (Post, 2002; Lamon, 2006; Steffe, Cobb, & von Glasersfeld, 1988; Wu, 2002), and suggests how that research can assist efforts to develop better understanding of fractions in college students. We also draw on the development of fractions in Singapore and Japan elementary mathematics curricula. This essay grew out of discussions at a workshop on teaching fractions at the Park City Mathematics Institute in July 2006.

Moving from whole numbers to fractions

Children develop an intuitive understanding of whole numbers in the context of counting objects. Because fractions and the arithmetic of fractions are much more complicated, intuition cannot be counted on to develop an understanding in a person's mind of what fractions are, much less how to calculate with them. Notation and terminology are much more important with fractions, but they can cause more problems than they solve.

For learners of all ages, definitions of basic mathematical concepts have to be framed with care: not too formal and not too informal. The common sense notion of a whole number as a counting number, used to count how many items are in a collection, provides a reasonable definition. In anticipation of rational and real numbers, whole numbers may later be identified with appropriate points on the number line.

On the other hand, most naïve approaches to understanding of a fraction, such as 1/3, can lead to misperceptions. Thinking of 1/3 in terms of a circle split into three thirds is a helpful place to start but can cause problems. A person with this image of 1/3 might forget that the pieces need to be equal and think of 1/3 as the name of one of the pieces when a circle split into 3 unequal pieces. This circle-based definition of 1/3 is not much help when one needs to find 1/3 of 24 pencils.

As soon as is judged feasible, a learner should be given the following definition of a fraction. This is the definition of a fraction used in many other *countries:*

A fraction is a number that is an integer multiple of some unit fraction.

In mathematical notation, we mean a number of the form $k(1/l)$, for whole numbers k, l ($l > 0$). This definition assumes that the person has first developed a good understanding of what a unit fraction is. Unit fractions are discussed extensively in the next section. Note that in the essay, we will not worry about more complicated fractions, with numerators and denominators that are themselves fractions or irrational numbers.

Independently of formal study of fractions, people encounter fractions in a variety of everyday situations—telling time, making change, cooking recipes, sharing (when portions are not whole amounts), and measuring small lengths. There are many diverse day-to-day *interpretations* of fractions. For a fraction like 2/3, the two most common interpretations are

1. Representing two of three equally divided parts.
2. Representing the quantity resulting from a measurement, such as 2/3 meter.

Note that the first interpretation is based on an unspecified whole. A danger with multiple interpretations of fractions is that may be viewed as equivalent definitions of fractions, heightening confusion about what a fraction is.

Defining fractions in terms of unit fractions avoids a major conceptual problem, namely, establishing that a fraction is a number. That burden now falls to unit fractions. A second advantage of defining fractions in terms of unit fractions is that this approach separates the study of the numerator and the denominator of a fraction. Numerators are standard counting numbers, while denominators are a totally new quantity—they are units defined in terms of reciprocals. Again, this is the reason we focus in the rest of the article on unit fractions and units generally.

With so much time in early grades devoted to whole number arithmetic, students unconsciously reinforce their initial intuition that the term 'number' means only a 'whole number' or 'counting number.' A U.S. fourth grade student who has encountered fractions in measurement (time, money, lengths, etc.) and other contexts will still likely say that a fraction is not a number, but rather is a part of something. Many adults would probably say the same thing. The Rational Number Project devoted considerable effort to understanding the hurdles to learning fractions created by students' belief that 'number' = 'whole number.' A similar problem arises with multiplication, which is initially learned as repeated addition, i.e., multiplication by a whole number. In this context, multiplication by a fraction makes no sense.

Because so many U.S. students never move beyond thinking of a number as a counting number, we should not be surprised that students mindlessly memorize operations with fractions in terms of the integers in the numerators and denominators of fractions without knowing what a fraction is or that they will assert that $1/3 + 1/5 = 1/8$.

On the other hand, a child's first understanding of a number will necessarily be as a counting number and multiplication is naturally introduced as repeated addition. Thus the pedagogical goal must be *to help students extend, rather than abandon, these initial understandings of a number and multiplication*; Les Steffe calls this critical process *reconceptualization*. Students face this challenge over and over as they advance in their mathematical education.

Students do develop a valid understanding of fractions as numbers in practical settings. For example, people know that one fourth of a particular item (e.g., of a pie or a quart) plus two fourths of that item equals three fourths of the item. Further, these students can often find natural common units for adding fractions in familiar contexts, e.g., half an hour plus a third of an hour equals 50 minutes.

Teaching students of any age a true understanding of fractions can build on their experience with fractions as parts of something and their readiness to do simple calculation with fractions. However, it is a big step, with which education researchers continue to grapple, to go from thinking about fractions as parts of given objects, such as pies, to thinking about fractions as potential parts of an unspecified object.

We close this section by mentioning the ambiguity in the notation for fractions. The expression a/b, where a, b are whole numbers and $b > 0$, has two mathematical meanings. It is a rational number equal to the fraction $a(1/b)$. It is also a common way of writing the calculation $a \div b$. Students need to have a good understanding of fractions (the first interpretation) before the relationship between fractions and division (the second interpretation) is presented. If fractions are presented in the context of division, students can easily think of a fraction not as number in its own right, but rather as the quotient of whole number division. In this flawed framework, it makes sense to learn arithmetic operations on fractions by memorizing integer-valued formulas for the resulting numerators and denominators. On the other hand, division naturally arises early in the discussion of fractions, e.g., finding 1/4 of some collection, such as 12 eggs. How division is best connected with learning fractions is an open challenge.

Unit fractions

Unit fractions, such as ¼, are a natural precursor to fractions. Unit fractions arise frequently in day-to-day conversations—a quarter (the coin), a quarter after 5 o'clock, a quarter of a mile down the road, a quarter of a cup of flour, a 1 ¼ inch screw, etc. A growing number of U.S. mathematics textbooks now discuss unit fractions to varying degrees starting in first grade.

For young children, unit fractions evolve from counting numbers: a pie divided into fourths is split into equal pieces which when counted amount to 4. Given two pies divided into sixths with 3 sixths left in the first pie (the three other sixths were eaten) and 2 sixths left in the second pie, first-grade students can count, and later add, the sixths in the two pies to obtain a total of 5 sixths.

Here is an activity (suggested by Yale mathematician Roger Howe) emphasizing the difference between counting numbers and unit fractions. Given a pitcher with a capacity of one quart of water, a student can determine the capacity, say 4 quarts, of a second pitcher by counting how many quart-size pitcherfuls it takes to fill up the new pitcher. Now consider a third pitcher whose capacity is 1/4th of a quart. To determine what this unit-fraction is, the student needs to determine how many pitcherfuls of the third pitcher it takes to fill the quart pitcher.

As noted above, while it natural to use pictures of pies or some other common geometric figures when starting to work with unit fractions, there are several misconceptions that can arise from such geometric examples of unit fractions. Extensive examples with measurement and with dividing a collection of items in equal shares can help students develop a more general mental understanding of unit fractions.

There are a number of different steps that extend this basic start with fractions. Intermixed with pictorial problems about unit fractions can be an occasional set of purely numerical problems (no figures) involving simple addition of fractions, such as 2/5 + 2/5. Another step is to have problems whose answers are improper fractions and then to restate an answer such as 5/4 cups of sugar as 1¼ cups of sugar. A parallel step is to have answers that are whole numbers, such as 4 fourths or 8 fourths, and to convert from fourths to whole numbers. Likewise, one can do conversions from whole numbers to unit fractions. Simple examples of multiplication and division of amounts stated in unit fractions can be introduced, e.g., given a recipe requiring 2 fourths of a cup of sugar, how many batches of the recipe can we make with two cups of sugar. Initially these problems would be accompanied with diagrams to help organize students' thinking.

These arithmetic experiences are reinforced and extended by the use of unit fractions in measurement problems. It is important that all whole number arithmetic be interpreted in terms of measuring lengths, e.g., addition is concatenation of lengths; multiplication is repeated concatenation of lengths. Thus the number line has a natural interpretation as distances from 0 (the start point). Unit fractions arise naturally in measuring lengths. Unit fractions also have a natural role in the measurement of time, money, and later area and volume. Note that the transition from multiplication by whole numbers, i.e., repeated addition, to multiplication by fractions is a natural extension in linear measurements: if bricks are 8 inches long, how would long would a row of 3½ bricks be?

While standard rulers are subdivided into halves, fourths, eighths, and sometimes sixteenths of an inch, students should have access to rulers with different types of subdivisions, e.g., in 5ths and in 10ths of an inch. In measuring lengths, students are initially equating whole numbers with lengths. Over time, it becomes natural to view all lengths as numbers, and an intuitive feeling for numbers as points on the number line develops. This is why Berkeley mathematician Hung-Hsi Wu likes to define fractions in terms of the number line.

When fractions are discussed in a collegiate quantitative literacy course, students are unlikely to be familiar with the definition of a fraction as a multiple of a unit fraction. The newness of this approach can be an excuse to review quickly several steps in the development sketched in the preceding paragraphs. It is important constantly to pose unit fractions problems in applied settings so that the 'unit' in 'unit fraction' has meaning. An example is how high will a pile of 4 notebooks be if each notebook is 5/8″ thick. The answer would first be found in terms of 1/8ths and then converted to whole inches. A more advanced, inverse version of this problem would be, how many notebooks that are 5/8″ thick can be piled into a box that is 2½ feet deep.

We noted above that unit fractions are derived in students' minds from counting numbers as follows: a pie divided into fourths is split into equal pieces which count to 4. To give a sense of the cognitive challenge students face in moving beyond this image of unit fractions, we cite a scene from a demonstration class of fifth graders led by Deborah Ball at the Park City Mathematics Institute in summer 2006. When students were asked to go to the blackboard and highlight 1/8th of a collection of 24 circles that had been drawn, one student first divided 8 into 24 to get 3, and then he proceeded to partition the set of 24 circles into groups of 3. He had to check that 8 groups of 3 balls completely partitioned the set of 24 balls before being able to say that 3 balls were 1/8 of the set of 24 balls. That is, the concept of 1/8 of a something, and implicitly the general concept of a unit fraction, did not exist in his thinking. He only could conceive of dividing something into 8 equal parts, a concept based on counting numbers.

Here is another example of the trouble that students have in moving beyond the equal division model (Tzur, 2006). Consider the two rectangles on the right, both with the same dimensions. The upper one is divided into 4 equal sections. The lower one is divided into 8 unequal sections. We are told that section A in the upper rectangle 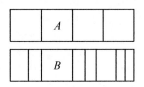 is the same size as section B in the lower rectangle. The question is, what fraction of the lower rectangle is section B?

Many middle school students and their teachers will assert that section B is our fourth of the upper rectangle but that one cannot tell what fraction it is of the lower rectangle. Many adults may have the same problem. This example shows the limitations of pictorial models of fractions.

Units

To illustrate the role of units in working with fractions, consider the following problem:

> Some balls are taken from a box and 15 balls are left. This number 15 is three quarters of the number of balls that started in the box. How many balls started in the box?

The reasoning for solving this problem involves two types of units. The problem can be restated: if we know 3 fourths of a quantity, what is 4 fourths of the quantity. The key is to think in terms of fourths. If one fourth is our unit, then the problem comes, if three units equal 15, what do four units equal. The natural intermediate step in the solution is to determine what one unit equals. We get that one unit is $15 \div 3 = 5$, balls, and the boxful of 4 units equals $4 \times 5 = 20$ balls.

While fourths were the units for initially analyzing the problem, 5's were the units involved in determining the final answer. One could say that one unit equals our fourth of a boxful, and then restate that unit as equal to 5 balls. One could also look at these two units as a ratio: 5 balls per fourth of a boxful. Analyzing relationships between two or more units underlies the solution of almost all real-world problems involving fractions. Many educators refer to the (implicit or explicit) use of units to solve such a problem as multiplication reasoning. Such reasoning is a prerequisite to solving fraction problems.

The problem could also be modeled algebraically as $(3/4)x = 15$ and solved for x to obtain $x = 15 \div (3/4)$, with the right-hand side computed with the invert-and-multiply rule for division by fractions. That rule, of course, yields the same calculation as in the previous analysis: divide 15 by 3 and multiply the result by 4 (or the order could be inverted). It is preferable that students be able to perform the reasoning described above than that they memorize (and soon forget) the invert-and-multiply rule for fraction division.

One learning aid heavily used in East Asian countries is diagrams. The 1999 TIMSS Video Study (NCES, 2003) found that 83% of the problems in 8th grade mathematics lessons in Japan used diagrams or drawings while the percentage in the U.S. was just 26%. For example, when problems like the one above are first encountered, students would see a diagram like the one on the right to point them towards the solution. College students who are being reacquainted with fractions should be asked to draw similar diagrams to help their initial reasoning.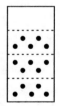

Many rate problems have a similar structure to the problem about balls in a box. For example:

> If a car going at a constant speed covers 48 miles in ¾ of an hour,
> how far will it go in one hour? Or equivalently, how fast is it going
> (in miles per hour)?

To solve this we must first focus on measuring time in fourths of an hour. Then we switch to the dual unit of 16 miles, the distance traveled in a fourth of an hour.

A nice grammatical analogy, often attributed to Ken and Herb Gross, is sometimes helpful for understanding the relationship between numbers and units. They call numbers 'adjectives' and they initially use these 'adjectives' only in the context of modifying a 'noun' such as 5 pencils or 2/3rds of a pie. The nouns are then extended to include units of measurement and units defined in terms of other adjective-noun pairs such as 4 (boxes of 500 pencils) and 5 (eighths of an inch).

Converting between units

One of the critical mathematical building blocks for working with fractions is equivalent fractions, different fractions that represent the same rational number, e.g., ½ or 2/4 or 5/10 or 13/26, etc. However, the general topic of equivalent representations of a quantity arises repeatedly in measurement problems, e.g., ½ foot = 6 inches, or 50 cents = 10 nickels = 5 dimes = 2 quarters = ½ dollar, as does the issue of finding a new, common representation for adding quantities in different units, e.g., adding 1/3 foot + ¼ foot by converting to inches, or adding 2 dimes and 1 quarter by converting to cents.

Equivalent fractions are a particular case of a more general mathematics topic, namely converting a number expressed in terms of one unit to another unit. Finding a new unit for representing different quantities arises in word problems involving multiplication and division.

Consider the problem:

A brick is 8 inches long. How many bricks must be placed end to end to reach 10 feet?

First we express the length of 10 feet in terms of inches—120 inches—using the conversion rule 1 foot = 12 inches. This is the first change of units. Then we convert the length in inches into another unit, brick lengths, using the conversion rule 1 brick length = 8 inches. The first conversion involved a multiplication and the second a division.

The following solution strategy follows the spirit of unit fraction examples in the previous section. After noting that one brick length is 2/3rds of a foot, one converts the total length from feet to 1/3rds of a foot. This is an easy conversion—multiply by 3—to keep straight in one's mind, and work with unit fractions continually reinforces such conversion strategies. So now the length is 30 1/3rds of a foot. Since each brick is 2 1/3rds of a foot long, we need 30/2 = 15 bricks.

The roles of the units can be inverted. We look at the problem in terms of brick lengths per foot: 1 foot = 1½ brick lengths. Then 10 feet = 1½ × 10 = 15 brick lengths. This problem illustrates the fact that *any time we perform multiplication or division in solving an applied problem, we are explicitly or implicitly converting units.* Moreover, there are a number of choices for units. In this case, inches, feet, and brick-lengths.

Let us recast this problem in a business setting. Given that an adult pays $40 for admission to an amusement park, what level of attendance is needed to generate $100,000 in a day? Answer: 100,000/40 = 2,500 adults. If one wanted to plan for the level of services needed in the park and the cost of these services, then one would probably find it useful to think simultaneously in terms of multiples of 2,500 people (demand) and $100,000 (available income). A natural extension of this problem would incorporate the fact that children pay, say, $30 for admission. Now many ratios of income and expenses come into play in analyzing demands and income from various mixes of adults and children.

Let us next consider a word problem involving three units. (It is the first word problem to appear in the 5th grade Singapore mathematics textbook (Singapore Math, 1997)):

> Mrs. Li bought 420 mangoes for $378. She packed them into packets of 4 mangoes each and sold all the mangoes at $6 per packet. How much money did she make?

The initial units that appear in the problem statement are mangoes and dollars. Later in the problem statement, packets enter. We need to convert units for measuring mangoes from individual mangoes to packets of 4 mangoes. Given that 4 mangoes go into packet, we divide 420 by 4 to obtain 105 packets. Now we convert our units for measuring mangoes from packets to value in dollars. The conversion factor is that one packet yields $6 dollars, and so we multiply for this conversion to obtain a value of $105 \times \$6 = \$630$. Finally, we have cost and income in the comparable units, dollars, and so the amount of money made in this activity, $630 - $378, can be computed.

Another way to approach this problem is to look for a way to convert directly from units of mangoes to units of money. This conversion requires determining a rate of income per mango. Since 4 mangoes in a packet sell for $6, we obtain a rate of $6/4 (= $1½ per) per mango.

This problem illustrates the fact that *calculation with a fraction can frequently be recast as a short cut for a two-step calculation involving a multiplication and a division with whole numbers.*

Let us now use units-based reasoning to analyze the following problem of fraction multiplication: $2/3 \times 4/5 = ?$. Interpreting 2/3 as 2 thirds [$= 2(1/3)$], we first need to find 1/3 of 4 fifths. We are initially stuck because 1/3 of 4 is not a whole number. We change to a new unit that is sure to work, namely $1/(3 \times 5)$. So we convert 4 fifths to 12 fifteenths [$= 12(1/15)$]. We can find 1/3 of 12 fifteenths by dividing 12 by 3; it is 4 fifteenths (4/15). Finally we multiply this amount by 2 to find $2 \times [4(1/15] = 8/15$. Diagrams can help with this problem. For example, 4/5 could initially be depicted with a rectangle partitioned by horizontal lines into 5 equals parts with the lower four parts shadowed. Then the rectangle could be subdivided with 3 vertical lines into 15 equals parts. One third of the 12 shadowed parts is found, etc.

Students' knowledge about units can also be used to revisit whole number addition and subtraction and to appreciate the role of conversion among decimal units in the standard algorithms of arithmetic. The place value notation is now seen as a system of related decimal units. The key steps of carrying in addition and borrowing in subtraction involve converting between consecutive decimal units. The standard multiplication and division algorithms can be studied in terms of how they combine partial computations in different decimal units.

We conclude this section with an important subtlety about the role of units in division. People often say that division is the 'inverse' operation of multiplication. However, there are two very distinct interpretations of how division is the 'inverse' of multiplication. Interpreting multiplication as repeated addition, the equation $4 \times 5 = 20$ says that the sum of four 5's is 20. Inverting this process, $20 \div 5 = 4$ could be interpreted as saying that 4 is the number of 5's that need to be summed to get 20. What then is the interpretation of $20 \div 4 = 5$ in terms of the multiplication $4 \times 5 = 20$? It is, what number when summed 4 times yields 20. A more familiar way to state this is, when we divide 20 into 4 equal parts, what is the size of each part. The first problem $20 \div 5 = 4$ was a change of units: we count numbers by 5's instead of by 1rs. The second problem is a partitioning situation, although it can also be interpreted with a change of units as follows: what should the units be if we want to 4 units to equal 20.

Concluding remarks

In this essay I have tried to make the case that understanding fractions well by relating them to units is both important and intellectually rich. It is definitely worthy of a college level course in quantitative literacy. More generally, fractions are a much richer mathematical construct than most people realize. This complexity is reflected in the fact that mastery of fractions was not normally required for university admission just 100 years ago, only whole number arithmetic was required (DeTurck, 2000).

However, today fractions arise frequently in daily life as percentages, rates and proportions. The details of teaching these applications of fractions to college students have been well explored by many others in the quantitative literacy movement. What is not as well appreciated is their connection to multi-step, whole-number word problems, as presented in this essay.

We note that greater attention to units also brings mathematics instruction closer to science instruction, where units play such an important role.

We close with a concrete example of the challenges in implementing the program outlined above. We refer again to the Park City model class of Deborah Ball's where students were asked to find one eighth of 24 balls drawn on the blackboard. One student divided 8 into 24, and, based on his answer of 3, partitioned the 24 balls into 3 groups of 8 each. Next he marked one ball in the first group of 8. However, the student then stopped and gave 1 as the answer. A cognitive specialist watching the students speculated what had gone wrong. Like many other students of his age, this student had trouble keeping track of more than two units at one time. He reorganized the problem of finding 1/8th of the whole group of 24 by first breaking 24 into 3 groups (units) of 8's. He then determined what 1/8th of a group of 8 was, but had lost track of the relationship between the original group of 24 and the group of 8.

Keeping track of multiple units is an example of a critical cognitive skill that mathematicians generally take for granted. Thus, to better prepare students to learn fractions, one needs not only to understand the proper mathematical development of underlying concepts, such as units, but also to understand the hurdles that students face when they try to learn these concepts.

References

DeTurck, D. (2000). Talk on the history of mathematics at the University of Pennsylvania.

Lamon, S. (2006). *Teaching fractions and ratios for understanding.* Mahwah, NJ: Lawrence Erlbaum Associates.

National Center for Education Statistics. (2003). *Teaching mathematics in seven countries: Results from the TIMSS 1999 video study.* Washington DC: Author.

Post, T. (2002). *The rational number project.* University of Minnesota College of Education and Human Development. cehd.umn.edu/rationalnumberproject.

Schaar, R. (2005). Oral presentation at Park City Mathematics Institute workshop.

Singapore Primary Mathematics 5A. (1997). Singapore: Federal Publication for the Curriculum Planning & Development Division, Ministry of Education.

Steffe, L. P., Cobb, P., & von Glasersfeld, E. (1988). Construction of arithmetical meanings and strategies. New York, NY: Springer-Verlag.

Tzur, R. (2006). Personal communication.

Wu, H.H. (2002). *Fractions.* Manuscript available at www.math.berkeley/~wu.

Quantitative Literacy and School Mathematics: Percentages and Fractions

Milo Schield
Augsburg College[*]

The secondary school mathematics curriculum emphasizes algebra as a necessary preparation for college calculus and statistics. Approximately 40% of college graduates, however, are in non-quantitative majors that do not require calculus or statistics and have little need for algebra beyond proportional and linear reasoning. Yet the elementary school curriculum presents common fractions symbolically as an introduction to high school algebra. This approach may "turn off" some very bright students, both those who might otherwise be interested in careers in science, technology, engineering and mathematics (STEM) and those who may graduate from college with majors such as journalism or political science that do not require much mathematics. Even non-STEM students need to be quantitatively literate to excel in their fields and to be capable citizens in a modern data-based democracy where most social and political issues involve quantitative reasoning.

To increase the effectiveness of quantitative literacy throughout the school curriculum, this paper explores the possibility of delaying, minimizing, or eliminating the manipulation of common fractions as mathematical objects and

[*] Milo A. Schield is professor of Business Administration and Director of the W. M. Keck Statistical Literacy Project at Augsburg College in Minneapolis, Minnesota. For the past ten years he has been developing a specialized course in statistical literacy for students majoring in the liberal arts. His articles on Statistical Literacy have appeared in *Peer Review* (a publication of the AAC&U) and in the *Proceedings of the American Statistical Association*. He has given invited talks at conferences sponsored by the International Association for Statistical Educators (IASE) and the International Statistical Institute (ISI). He has taught critical thinking at both the undergraduate and graduate level. Dr. Schield has a PhD in physics from Rice University and is Vice President of the National Numeracy Network. *E-mail*: schield@augsburg.edu

of replacing it with a more applied study of fractions in the context of percentages and rates.

- A greater focus on percentages and rates could enhance the quantitative literacy of all students and improve the motivational support provided by parents and teachers while still introducing important topics such as scaling, conversion, changing units, and symbolic notation.
- A greater focus on the ordinary English grammar involved in communicating about rates and percentages would allow students to become better consumers of information presented in tables and graphs.
- A greater focus on the uses of ratios would allow educators to prepare students for more advanced topics such as standardizing and Simpson's paradox that are common in everyday media but rarely covered in the current school curriculum.

This paper also discusses the possibility of introducing these quantitative literacy topics either as a pre-algebra bridging course or as a quantitative or statistical literacy course in place of algebra II for those students interested in non-quantitative majors in college.

Goals of mathematics education

The National Council of Teachers of Mathematics (NCTM), the principal professional society for K–12 mathematics education, says that its goal is to ensure "mathematical learning of highest quality for all students" (NCTM, 2007). This broad goal leaves open the choice of topics students should learn and the order in which they should be learned. In practice, it appears that elementary school mathematics prepares school children for high school mathematics, which in turn prepares students for college mathematics. Thus, the choice and order of topics at the school level may be influenced—if not driven—by the mathematical needs of students at college.

The mathematical needs of college students can be inferred from the mathematics and statistics courses they take—data that is gathered regularly by a survey by the Conference Board of the Mathematical Sciences (CBMS). According to the 2000 CBMS survey (Lutzer, D, J., J. W. Maxwell, & Rodi, 2002) of U.S. four-year colleges during the 2000 fall semester:

- 217,000 students took remedial mathematics [General Mathematics (30,000), Elementary Algebra (70,000) and Intermediate Algebra (117,000)];
- 723,000 took introductory pre-calculus mathematics [College Algebra

(211,000), Elementary Functions (105,000), Mathematics for Liberal Arts (86,000), Finite Mathematics (82,000) and Mathematics for Elementary School Teachers (68,000)];

- 297,000 took Calculus I; and
- 155,000 took Elementary Statistics in mathematics/statistics departments.

The courses most frequently mentioned by departments of mathematics as one of the top three courses taken by K–3 education majors were a multi-term mathematics course designed for elementary education majors (48%), followed by College Algebra (42%), Mathematics for Liberal Arts (39%), a single-term mathematics course designed for elementary education students (32%), and statistics (29%). The courses most frequently mentioned by departments of statistics as one of the top three statistics courses taken by K-3 education majors were elementary statistics (63%), statistical literacy (33%), and a single-term statistics course for elementary education majors (26%).

While the CBMS survey is the most accurate survey available of mathematics and statistics courses taken by U.S. college students, it has three limitations. First, it is a fall-only survey, so courses that are taught year-round (e.g., college algebra and statistics) may have different year-round enrollments than those taught primarily in the fall (e.g., Calculus I). Second, it does not count those students or courses taught outside mathematics and statistics departments. This is a problem for statistics at four-year colleges since statistics is often also taught in other departments such as business, psychology, and sociology. Or as the CBMS report noted, "in fall 2000 there were fewer than 100 statistics departments in the U.S., and almost 1,400 mathematics departments. Consequently the numbers reported by statistics departments would not include the students from the vast majority of colleges." Third, there is no way to link courses with students—we cannot calculate what percentage of college graduates take a given course as their last course in mathematics. For example, college algebra may be taken as a prerequisite for calculus by some and as a terminal course for others.

These three limitations of the CBMS survey are important in identifying the reasons that college students take a mathematics course. Is it because of general education requirements, the requirements of their majors, their personal interests, or their need for remedial courses as a prerequisite for any of the foregoing?

An alternate approach to identifying the mathematical needs of college students is to examine bachelor's degrees earned by major. In 2003, there were 1.35 million bachelor's degrees awarded at U.S. four-year colleges and universities (U.S. Census Bureau, 2006, Table 289). If we assume that calculus was taken by all students graduating in science, technology, engineering and mathematics (STEM), then 12% of college graduates were required to take calculus. If we assume that statistics was taken by all students graduating in business, the social sciences, psychology, health sciences and biology, then 48% of college graduates were required to take statistics. Even though some students may take calculus or statistics even if not required by their major, and some majors may require calculus as a prerequisite for statistics, this leaves approximately 40% of college graduates with majors that do not generally require a specific mathematics course. These non-quantitative majors include education, visual and performing arts, communication and journalism and English, as well as the liberal arts, humanities, general studies and interdisciplinary studies. Many of these students must take one or more college mathematics courses as part of their general education requirements. But the lack of a specific mathematics requirement may tell students in these non-quantitative majors that their major department sees no direct benefit of mathematics for their major.

Even the role of mathematics in general education is changing. At some schools, college algebra no longer satisfies a quantitative general education requirement. For example, Arizona State University recently removed college algebra from the list of courses students can use to fulfill the numeracy requirements for general studies. "The department has taken this action because it believes students requiring only one mathematics course in their college experience should be introduced to mathematics that is more applied in nature. We further believe any student taking college algebra should have every intention of taking another mathematics course " (Isom, 2004). Briggs (2006) reviews the "algebra dilemma" in designing a successful liberal arts mathematics course and argues that "less could be better." He suggests that we should "avoid doing algebra when there is no ulterior purpose and let the applications determine the necessary mathematics."

Unfortunately, there is no summary of the mathematics courses required for general education at U.S. colleges and universities. Courses such as college algebra, statistics, mathematics for liberal arts, quantitative literacy and statistical literacy are often used for this purpose along with courses designated as satisfying a quantitative reasoning requirement. For a review of the topics commonly found in quantitative literacy courses, see Gillman (2006) for a mathematics-centered review and Madison (2006) and Schield (2004a) for a broader view.

Overlaid on the issue of students' mathematical needs is the issue of attitudes towards mathematics. All too many students have a negative attitude toward mathematics. The Third International Mathematics and Science Study

(TIMSS, 1999, Exhibit 4.10) found that 35% of the U.S. 8th graders surveyed say they have a positive attitude toward mathematics, 50% say their attitude is between negative and positive (neutral) toward mathematics and 15% say they have a negative attitude. For the girls in this study, the percentages were 32%, 52% and 16%, respectively. Since these 8th graders typically have not yet had algebra or geometry, a relevant explanation may be the teaching of fractions.

Mathematics for the other 40%

School mathematics has many goals, one of which is to provide students with the mathematical concepts and training they need to function as quantitatively literate citizens in a modern democracy. Training students to study mathematics or science in college is another goal. But if this STEM goal conflicts with the quantitative literacy goal, the algebra-centered school mathematics curriculum may become dysfunctional. It may inadvertently encourage bright college bound—but non-mathematics oriented—students to avoid quantitative thinking even when it is appropriate and important.

The 40% of college graduates with non-quantitative majors are more likely to become elementary school teachers, journalists, lawyers, policy makers and religious, social and political leaders. These are the students who are likely to take courses with titles like Mathematics for Liberal Arts and Statistical Literacy. These liberal arts majors may not need an algebra-centered curriculum to help them reason quantitatively, that is, to form sound arguments and make informed decisions about matters for which numerical evidence is offered. But all too many humanities majors are innumerate, or quantitatively illiterate. Among other deficiencies, they have surprising difficulty reading tables of percentages (Atkinson and Wills, 2007) and Schield (2006a).

Addressing this conflict does not mean supporting a watered-down mathematics curriculum for potential STEM students, rather, just the opposite. A slightly different approach to the teaching of fractions can teach quantitative relationships that are useful to non-STEM students, that can challenge STEM students, and that might even attract bright non-STEM students into STEM majors in college. A first step along this road is to identify the quantitative literacy needs of college-educated citizens, in particular, of students in the arts and humanities (e.g., English, history, philosophy, aesthetics, and political science).

Student weaknesses related to mathematics

Lutsky (2006) analyzed writing portfolios of 200 students at Carleton College, a highly selective liberal arts college. He found that a third of these college students failed to use quantitative reasoning (QR) when it should have been *central* to their analysis, and nine in ten failed to use quantitative reasoning when it was *peripheral* but of potential benefit to their argument.

An earlier analysis prepared for the International Association for Statistical Educators identified several categories of problems involving quantitative or statistical literacy (Schield, 2004b) as follows.

Problems comparing counts or amounts using ordinary English: Students know that "8 is 6 more than 2" and that "8 is 4 times [as much as] 2." But they may mistakenly think "8 is 400% more than 2." They are quite comfortable—but mistaken—in saying "2 is 4 times less than 8." They are amazed that 15% is 50% (but not 5%) more than 10%. When told that "Jane is half as old as Tom; Tom is twice as old as Mary" and asked if Jane and Mary are the same age, their answer, "Yes," is correct. When told that "Jane is 50% younger than Tom; Tom is 50% older than Mary" and asked if Jane and Mary are the same age, their answer, "Yes," is incorrect.

Problems describing percentages and rates in ordinary English: Percentage and rates are common in graphs, yet one study found that one college student in five could not correctly read the simple pie chart of percentages shown in Figure 1 (Schield, 2006a). Percentages were featured in 70% of the graphs in *USA Today On-Line Snapshots* (Schield 2006c), yet many students were unable to properly interpret their meaning as evidenced by Figures 2–5. In reading Figure 2, students mistakenly concluded that 24% of all adults have two dogs—rather than 24% of all dog owners have two dogs.

In Figure 3, some students thought the bar graph was wrong since the percentages add to more than 100%—not realizing that the alternatives were non-exclusive in the survey. In Figure 4, some students mistakenly concluded that 43% of the happy people surveyed are married rather than that 43% of the married people surveyed are happy.

In Figure 5, the percentages add to 92% and the age groups are exclusive (but not exhaustive), so students cannot tell whether 29% of those ages 21–25 received a DUI or 29% of those receiving a DUI are ages 21–25. In Figure 6,

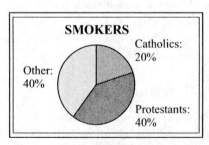

Figure 1. Pie Chart

Figure 2. Bar Chart (Sum = 100%)

Figure 3. Bar Chart (Sum > 100%)

Figure 4. Bar Chart (Sum < 100%)

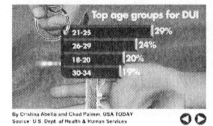

Figure 5. Bar Chart (Sum ~ 100%)

Figure 6. Bar Chart (Sum ~ 100%)

the percentages add to 98% and the income groups are exclusive and exhaustive so students cannot tell if 15% of guests from low-income households bring gifts or if 15% of guests who bring gifts are from low-income households.

Similar weaknesses are apparent in reading tables of rates and percentages. In reading Table 1, 19% of students surveyed mistakenly thought the circled 25% said that 25% of females are blacks rather than 25% of blacks are female (Schield, 2006a). In reading Table 2, among those surveyed, 55% of students, 53% of professional data analysts and 30% of college faculty mistakenly thought the circled 20% said that 20% of runners are female smokers (or did not know) rather than 20% of female smokers are runners. These error rates are important since percentages and rates were featured in 40% of the tables in the 1997 U. S. Statistical Abstract.

College students also have considerable difficulty determining part and whole in ratios presented in tables and graphs. In reading Table 3, students

	SEX		
RACE	Male	Female	TOTAL
Black	75%	25%	100%
White	50%	50%	100%
Other	40%	60%	100%
TOTAL	50%	50%	100%

Table 1. 10% Row Table

PERCENTAGE WHO ARE RUNNERS			
	Non-smoker	Smoker	Total
Female	50%	20%	40%
Male	25%	10%	20%
Total	37%	15%	30%

Table 2. Two-way half table

were asked to describe the 59.3%
in the cell for black males. About
a third of the students mistakenly
concluded that 59.3% of overweight or obese adults were black
males rather than that 59.3% of
black male adults are overweight

Adults	Men	Women	Total
Total	53.5	40.5	48
Whites	52.9	39.7	46.1
Blacks	59.3	49.6	54.4
Other	51.4	40.8	46

Table 3. Percentage overweight or obese

or obese. They seemingly ignored that this incorrect statement was highly dis-
proportional since less than 7% of U.S. adults are black males. They ignored
the fact that the table Totals are averages—not sums.

Augsburg College students studying statistical literacy have difficulty
interpreting percentages when they are expressed in ordinary English. They
are not sure if "the percentage of men who are runners" is the same as "the
percentage of men among runners." When given "20% of men who run are
smokers," they often conclude that "20% is the percentage of men who run
who are smokers." They cannot see a difference between "the percentage of
male runners who smoke" and "the percentage of men who run and smoke."
They are exposed to sports grammar (e.g., "percentage of passes completed"
or "percentage of completed passes") where there is a natural whole so the
syntax is irrelevant and both have the same meaning. Without training, they
don't see that "the percentage of male smokers" has no natural whole and
could be "the percentage of males who are smokers" or "the percentage of
smokers who are male."

Problems comparing percentages and rates using ordinary English: A
study involving Figure 1 dealing with the incidence of smoking in relation
to Protestant/Catholic identity found that 60% of students and data analysts
surveyed mistakenly concluded from this table that "Protestants (40%) are
twice as likely to be smokers as are Catholics (20%)" (Schield, 2006a). A
correct statement would be, "Protestants (40%) are twice as likely among
smokers as are Catholics." The comparison of ratios, rates and percentages
in ordinary language requires using English in a very precise manner. Small
changes in syntax can produce large changes in semantics.

Problems involving weighted averages of measurements or percentages: Steen
(2001, pp. 11) described "understanding the behavior of weighted averages
used in ranking colleges, cities, products, investments and sports teams" as a
key topic in quantitative literacy for citizenship. Students in non-quantitative
majors may not realize that many of the statistics we read are not simple
averages—they are weighted averages where the average depends on the
number in each component of the mixture.

College students have trouble comparing weighted averages for two groups with different mixtures in their respective populations. Supposing we find that the average weight of college seniors at St Thomas is 30 pounds more than the seniors at St. Catherine's. This could be an indication of overweight or obesity at St. Thomas. But students at St Catherine's college are mainly women while those at St. Thomas are equally split. The 30 pound difference could reflect different mixtures, that is, the difference in the number of men and women at the two colleges.

College students have even more difficulty with weighted averages when they involve two groups with different mixtures and when both the outcome and the mixture are expressed as percentages. Suppose the percentage of college students who go on to graduate school is much higher at St. Thomas than at Augsburg. This might reflect a difference in the quality of the education. But it might reflect a difference in the mixture of students. Suppose that children of college-educated parents are more likely to go to graduate school than children whose parents are not college educated. Suppose that college-educated parents are more prevalent among students at St. Thomas than among students at Augsburg. The failure to take into account the influence of this third factor— college educated parents—can confound the association between the two colleges and the percentage of their graduates who go on to graduate school.

Figure 7 illustrates a graphical technique for illustrating and standardizing weighted averages.

Consider the death rates at two hospitals: City and Rural. The overall death rate at each depends on the death rates for the two groups of patients:

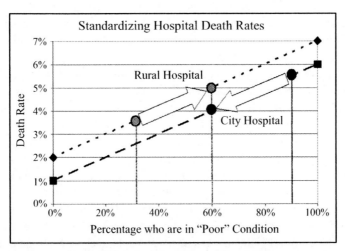

Figure 7. Standardizing Hospital Death Rates

those in poor condition (right side) and those in good condition: those not in poor condition (left side). The overall average is a weighted average—the average of the death rate for the two groups weighted by their prevalence: the percentage of patients who are in poor condition (horizontal axis).

In this case, the overall death rate is higher at a City Hospital (5.5%) than at a Rural Hospital (3.5%). Obviously patients in poor condition (right side) are much more likely to die than those in good condition (left side). Patient condition could be confounded with the hospitals and thereby influence the observed association between hospitals and death rates. Suppose that patients in poor condition are much more prevalent among patients at City Hospital (90%) than among those at Rural Hospital (30%).

When given the death rates for patients in poor and good condition for each hospital, students can standardize the prevalence of the confounder to the overall average (60%) and see that in this case the standardized death rate is reversed. The standardized death rate—the death rate obtained after taking into account the influence of a related confounder of patient condition—is now higher at Rural Hospital (5%) than at City Hospital (4%). This reversal is an example of Simpson's Paradox—a phenomenon that is all too common in everyday comparisons of averages, rates and percentages. This simple graphical technique illustrates how one can take into account the influence of a third factor on an average, a rate or a percentage.

More examples can be found in Schield (2006b) and Terwilliger and Schield (2004). Lesser (2001) provides a comprehensive review of weighted averages—the basis of Simpson's paradox.

Problems concerning student attitudes. It may seem inappropriate to include attitudes when determining content, especially among primary school students, but by secondary school, if not by middle school, student attitudes affect student choices and performance.

Business majors at Augsburg College in spring 2003 were surveyed by the author on their major within business and on their attitude toward mathematics. Majors were classified in two groups: non-quantitative (management, international business, management information systems and marketing) or quantitative (accounting and finance). Attitudes toward mathematics were classified into two groups: "like math" (strongly like or like) and "dislike math" (neutral, dislike or strongly dislike). The result: 30% of quantitative majors and 70% of non-quantitative majors "dislike" mathematics. Almost 60% (40%/70%) of the students in management, international business, MIS or marketing are attributable to their dislike of mathematics. Note that this association does not say that their attitude toward mathematics *caused* students to choose non-quantitative majors, but the association suggests and supports this claim.

Attitudes are important in another way. Schau (2003) noted, "Many of us believe that attitudes impact students' achievement, [their] course completion, [their] future course enrollment, and [their] statistical thinking outside of the classroom." The less value students see in what they are learning, the less motivated they are to participate, to learn, to remember what they learned, and to use what they learned.

Interestingly, Schau found that college students see less value in studying statistics after completing the introductory research-oriented statistics course than they did before taking the course. It may be that high school students see less value in mathematics after taking algebra than they did before. It may be that grade school students see less value in mathematics after studying fractions than they did before. If this were so, it would represent a serious problem—even if immaturity is the underlying cause. Student attitudes affect their willingness to take further courses in a subject. Those grade-school children who see less value in mathematics are less likely to take the next courses in mathematics or, if required to do so, their performance may reflect their negative attitude. In the end, they may be far less likely to pursue STEM majors in college.

School students may not like multiplication or division, and they may not see much value in these operations immediately. But their teachers, parents and older peers are generally united in claiming that these skills are important— even in the age of computers and calculators. But when students and their older peers see little value in a subject such as manipulating fractions, students may start to question whether their teachers really have their best interests at heart.

'Attitudes' includes the attitudes of teachers and parents, which may account for much—if not most—of the difference in academic performance among K-6 school children. If teachers do not see the value in material required for a majority of their students, this may affect their attitude: they will not be excited about and persuasive in teaching such material. If parents do not think their children should learn the material, if they cannot see that the material is useful or how their children will benefit, their negative attitude may influence children in ways teachers cannot overcome.

Teachers may have more influence on student learning than does the choice of topics in a curriculum and parents may have more influence on student learning than do teachers.

Call for change

The NCTM has done much to review the mathematics curriculum, but more can be done to improve the school curriculum for the 40% of college students in non-quantitative majors.

Ideally the mathematics curriculum should help each student use their mind—at their level of understanding—to understand the world in quantitative terms. Mathematics provides some simple quantitative devices for taking into account related factors. Two-group comparisons take into account the size of a related factor chosen as the basis for the comparison either as a difference, a ratio or a percentage difference. Rates and percentages take into account the size of the group. Two-group comparisons of rates and percentages take into account both the different sizes of the two groups and the ratio for the group chosen as the basis for the comparison. Standardizing takes into account the influence of a related factor. Taking into account the influence of a related factor is what links the mathematics of percentages, rates, comparisons and standardization to quantitative literacy with its focus on mathematics in context.

Here are some recommendations:

1. Emphasize ordinary English. Mathematics educators should consider how ordinary English can be used in preparing students for algebra. Some might argue that the words of ordinary English cannot substitute for symbolic algebra. Yet English can convey quantitative ideas. Most—if not all—arithmetic operations and algebraic relationships can be expressed in ordinary sentences. Ordinary English can be used to make quantitative statements that are clear and unambiguous. Everyday graphics (e.g., pie and bar charts) can display the semantics of percentages just as Venn diagrams display the overlap between two groups or variables.

Including a wider-variety of ordinary English forms in teaching mathematical relationships may help improve the attitudes of school teachers and parents. Parents and teachers may encourage students to work harder in mathematics if they understand the value of what is being taught.

2. Distinguish percentages from fractions. Mathematics educators might rethink the relation between the teaching of percentages and the teaching of fractions. Teaching the manipulation of common fractions that are ratios of integers can provide an introduction to algebra which in turn provides a basis for calculus and statistics. But do college students in non-quantitative majors need to manipulate common fractions? They certainly need to manipulate percentages. But are percentages fractions?

Mathematically, percentages are fractions with a denominator of 100. But operationally percentages are not common fractions. To add common integer-ratio fractions such as ½ and ¾, one must scale at least one of the fractions to give them a common denominator so they can be added. But percentages—by their very nature—all have the same denominator: 100. There is never any need to rescale a percent before adding or subtracting. Operationally, percentages are much closer to integers or decimal fractions than they are to common fractions.

Consider a well-known mistake involving fractions: $1/3 + 1/5 = 2/8$. In making this mistake, students apply whole-number addition where it is not appropriate. But would students add 33% to 20% and get 25%? Not likely! The mistake with common fractions seldom occurs when the fractions have a common denominator.

3. Be aware of how students and adults—even very bright people—avoid common fractions. How do they do this when dealing with everyday units such as time, money, distance, weight and volume? One way is to shift to a smaller unit so the fraction becomes an integer. In this way, half an hour become 30 minutes, half a dollar becomes 50 cents, half a foot becomes 6 inches, half a pound becomes 8 ounces and a third of a tablespoon becomes a teaspoon. Percentages function in the same way: a tenth of a unit becomes 10 percent—where 'percent' (one-one hundredth) functions as the new smaller unit.

Of course one can always go smaller than the smallest common unit—be it a second, a cent, an inch, an ounce, a teaspoon or a percent. Are fractions required? Yes, but not as often and they may not be common fractions. We can use decimal fractions. *Mathematically, decimal fractions are a type of common fraction. Operationally, decimal fractions are closer to whole numbers than to common fractions.* Now this may be questionable if students mistakenly think $0.17 > 0.7$ because 17 is bigger than 7. But if the arithmetic of decimal fractions is easier than the arithmetic of common fractions—easier for teachers to teach, for parents to support and for students to learn,—then this would support the claim that decimal fractions are closer—operationally—to whole numbers than to common fractions.

Learning to add fractions with different denominators may be a critical step in a child's understanding of rational numbers. But do students in the humanities or educated citizens in a modern democracy need to distinguish rational numbers from irrational numbers? Do they need to know how to divide one common fraction by another when the few times they encounter this, they can convert them both to decimal fractions and use integer arithmetic to calculate the result?

There are three distinct situations that arise in adding common fractions:

- Those having identical denominators (e.g., percents with a denominator of "100," and rates with a common basis). Fractions having identical denominators are added by adding their numerators just like whole numbers for the same denominator (the same unit fraction). So, $1/4 + 3/4 = 4/4$ and 25% + 75% = 100%.

- Those having commensurate denominators (e.g., ½ + ¼). Those having commensurate denominators can be easily scaled so they have a common denominator. For example, consider $(a/b) + (c/d)$ where $d = k*b$ so $b = d/k$. Thus, $(a/b) + (c/d) = [(ak)/d)] + (c/d) = [(ak)+c]/d$. If we want to add a quarter and a half dollar, we exchange the half dollar for two quarters (divide the half dollar by ¼ to get two-fourths) and add the two quarters with the one quarter to get the total of three quarters. In shifting from dollars to quarters, it seems that students have difficulty seeing that multiplying the dollars by four is the same as dividing the dollars by ¼.
- Those having incommensurate denominators (e.g., 1/4 + 1/5). One can express the addition of incommensurate fractions as a result of a double scaling. Consider $(a/b) + (c/d)$. If b and d are incommensurate, then a simple scaling is to use their product. Scale (a/b) by multiplying and dividing by d; scale (c/d) by multiplying and dividing by b. This gives, $(ad)/(bd) + (cb)/(bd)$ which gives the well-known result $(ad + bc)/bd$.

4. Introduce arithmetic operations using percentages and rates in context.
Mathematicians create mathematical objects by omitting context. Quantitative literacy focuses on mathematical objects in context where the context makes a mathematical difference. Thus, ratios, fractions and percents encountered at school are typically mathematical objects. But the fractions, ratios, percentages and rates encountered in everyday usage typically appear in context. Eight-tenths or 80% is a mathematical object. "The percentage of U.S. toys that are made in China is 80%" is a percentage: a fraction in context where the numbers refer to things in reality. Likewise, a ratio of two dimensionless numbers is a mathematical object. A ratio in context (e.g., 30 miles per U.S. gallon or 12.8 kilometers per liter) is a ratio in context. As a mathematical object, a rate is simply a ratio. But the term 'rate' in context can mean a rate per unit time (the number of births per year), a prevalence (the unemployment rate among U.S. blacks 18-24 in the civilian labor force who are not in college was 18.3% in 2005) (U.S. Census Bureau, 2007, Table 581) or an incidence (the death rate is 817 per 100,000 U.S. population in 2004 (U.S. Census Bureau, 2007, Table 109)).

Any two real numbers can be added, subtracted, multiplied or divided. But the results are not always meaningful or appropriate for numbers in context.

Once students have identified that a percentage or rate involving counts of real things that can be identified by their membership in a group (e.g., men or women), then students can determine whether two percentages or rates have common or distinct parts. If they have distinct parts within a common whole, then their sum can be meaningful—provided these parts are exclusive. But if they have common parts involving two distinct wholes, then adding them may be meaningless. As an example, consider this problem. Suppose a company has a 60% market-share in the eastern U.S. and a 70% market-share in the Western US. What is their market-share in the entire US? It cannot be 130%. Here is a case where the addition of fractions (6/10 + 7/10 = 13/10) is correct but meaningless. Students need to be taught when a sum of fractions in context is meaningful and when it is not.

Fractions in context have different forms and the context determines what can and cannot be done operationally. The operations that can be done or not done are not always consistent from context to context. This makes it imperative that educators help students interpret fractions in context in a sense-making way rather than in an abstract algorithmic way.

5. Be aware of objections to increasing the focus on percentages and rates in context. It is all too easy to say that just because we may not do something in everyday life, that we should not have to learn it. Students used to learn how to take a square root, but now calculators do that for us. Does this mean students should not have to learn how to divide or multiply or subtract or add since calculators can do this for us? Absolutely not! Calculators do not tell us how to enter the information. Calculators do not provide an estimate of the answer so we can see that we made a mistake in entering the problem. Calculators may not help us develop a conceptual understanding that is crucial to becoming educated.

Wu (2002) claims that "fractions hold the potential for being the best kind of 'pre-algebra." He noted that, "the subject of fraction arithmetic—usually addressed in grades 5 and 6—is rife with opportunities for getting students comfortable with the abstraction and generality expressed through symbolic notation." He illustrated this in adding two fractions, $(a/b) + (c/d) = (ad+bc)/(bd)$, and noted the truth of this equation holds regardless of whether the variables are whole numbers, fractions, finite decimals or polynomials [assuming non-zero denominators]. The same holds true when multiplying two fractions: $(a/b)(c/d) = (ac)/(bd)$. For Wu, "there is no generality or abstraction without symbolic notation."

6. Identify advantages to other mathematical topics that might be introduced to help students develop their conceptual powers instead of common fractions. Taking Wu's claims as true, one can still ask if tables, graphs and ordinary English statements are a form of symbolic notation. One can ask if there are other mathematical ideas that could introduce students to abstraction and symbolic notation. Ratios (including simple percentages and rates), linear models ($y = a + bx$), weighted averages ($z = [x*$weight of $x] +$ [$y*$weight of y]) and scaling and proportional reasoning ($a/b = c/d$) can all be demonstrated using symbolic notation and are encountered more often in everyday life than adding common fractions.

Abstraction and generality are important in developing one's conceptual powers. Learning that the unit of measurement is a human choice is an important step in cognitive development. Are there ways to use fractions that are a more natural fit with the way people talk in everyday life?

Instead of using common fractions to introduce symbolic notation and the idea of scaling, one alternate might be to use everyday rates. Everyday rates are not mathematical rates: the slope of a line (y/x or dy/dx). Such a slope may be described as a 'grade' measured in percent.

Everyday rates are ratios of two related counts. They may be incidences per unit time such as birth rates and death rates, or prevalences at a moment in time such as the unemployment rate. Whereas percentages are all 'per 100,' these everyday rates specify the unit of measure. At first changing the scale seems no different with rates than with the everyday units of time. In the U.S., the birth rate in 2003 was 14 per 1,000 people (U.S. Statistical Abstract (2007, Table 76). Thus it is 140 per 10,000 people and 1,400 per 100,000 people.

But with real-world rates, the numerator and denominator are not necessarily two independent quantities: they are often linked. Men cannot give birth so the birth rate in the U.S. is 29 per 1,000 women—since women made up 51% of the population and 14/0.51 is 29. Women younger than 15 or older than 44 seldom give birth so the birth rate in the U.S. is 66 per 1,000 women aged 15–44—since 44% of all women are ages 15–44 and 29/0.44 is 66. (U.S. Statistical Abstract, 2007, Table 78). In these cases, the numerator in reality remains unchanged (U.S. births in 2003) and is independent of the size of the denominator (adults, women or women ages 15–44).

The linkage between numerator and denominator depends critically on the context. In a percentage, the numerator (the class counted) is always a subset of the denominator so changing the size or the group can change the numerator. The same is true for many rates. Thus, the accident rate per 100,000 licensed drivers is generally not the same as the accident rate per 100,000 cars or the accident rate per 100,000 bars. Recall the birth rates mentioned above. Women ages 18–19 are less than 10% of women age 15–44, but the birth rate for the younger group, 71 per 1,000 among women 18–19, is not ten times as high. Obviously the numerator—number of births among this age group—is less than the number of births among those women age 15–44. Using rates where the numerator and denominator are linked because of the context introduces a new factor that is not obvious in dealing with a common fraction a/b.

As another example, compare the accidental death rates between Arkansas and Hawaii in 1996. Arkansas has a higher accidental death rate than Hawaii (36 vs. 18) per 100,000 registered vehicles. But Hawaii has a higher accidental death rate than Arkansas (35 vs. 7) per 1,000 miles of road (U.S. Statistical Abstract, 1998, Tables 143, 1019 and 1029). Once again students see that the choice of the unit of measure not only changes the size of a statistic—it can influence the direction of an association. If students are to be statistically literate, they must understand that the numerator and denominator can be linked by the choice of the denominator—not just by the size of the unit in the denominator.

Scaling is mathematical. But if students are to be quantitatively literate, they need to learn that the choice of the group—the basis of a comparison—can strongly influence the size of a number or a statistic. Teaching fractions as having an independent numerator and denominator overlooks this dependency on context: a material element that is critical in the real world—and in the conditional probability of statistics.

It may be helpful for mathematical educators to use this focus on context to categorize the transformation of ratios. Consider three groups: numerator is directly proportional to denominator (shifting a rate from per 100 to per 1,000: mathematical scaling), numerator is independent of the denominator (shifting the birth rate from all people to just women), and the numerator is related to or dependent on the denominator but not directly proportional (shifting the accident rate denominator from registered vehicles to miles of road). By focusing just on the first group, students may have been denied access to more complex applications of mathematics that are relevant in everyday life.

Weighted averages provide another way to introduce abstraction. One wonders why the weighted average of counts in separate group, $[(a/b), (c/d)]$, is not included as $(a+c)/(b+d)$ since the weighted average is a real and valuable concept in everyday life. For example, if there are 30 smokers among 90 men and 5 smokers among 10 women, then there are a total of 35 smokers among these 100 individuals: 35% of these people are smokers. Note that the 35% is the average of the 33% among men and the 50% among women weighted for the mixture of men (90%) and women (10%): $0.9*33\% + 0.1*50\% = 35\%$.

In quantitative literacy, context counts. Even if ratios in context were inferior to mathematical objects such as common fractions in terms of introducing students to symbolic notation and abstraction, the benefits from a heightened focus on context along with improved teacher understanding and persuasiveness, from improved parental involvement and from increased student awareness of their benefits might more than compensate for their formal weaknesses having less emphasis on symbolic notation.

7. Identify places in the curriculum to introduce or embed the study of fractions in context. Eliminating the abstract algebra-like manipulation of common fractions in elementary schools may be overly drastic at this time. Consider three alternatives. The first is for all students taking mathematics in middle school. The last two are alternatives to algebra II for those students not planning on attending college or who are planning on non-quantitative majors in college—majors such as English, elementary education, history, political science, communications, journalism, music, art or philosophy.

- Introduce rates and percentages as presented in tables and graphs in middle school as a pre-algebra bridging course: a supplement to—or an application of—fractions.

- Introduce a Quantitative Literacy course as an alternative to algebra II. According to Gillman (2006), "there is consensus that the mathematical skills necessary to be quantitatively literate include elementary logic, the basic mathematics of financial interest, descriptive statistics, finite probability, an elementary understanding of change, the ability to model problems with linear and exponential models, estimations and approximation, and general problem solving." For more on such a course, see Gillman (2006) and Madison (2006).

- Introduce a Statistical Literacy course—evaluating statistical associations as evidence for causal connections—as an alternative to Algebra II. In addition to teaching students about rates, percentages, comparisons and standardization as devices for taking into account the influence of context, Statistical literacy could include a stronger focus on the influence of chance and include the influence of social construction —the choices made in defining groups or measures, in combining subgroups and in presenting statistical results in graphs, tables and in words. See Best (2001, 2002, 2004 and 2007) and Schield (2007a). For an overview of a Statistical Literacy course, see Schield (2004a, 2007b) and Isaacson (2005). This statistical literacy course could serve as a bridging course for those students wanting to take AP Statistics in high school.

8. Identify and teach topics that college students in non-quantitative majors need to master at the school level and which are currently not being taught there. Mastering percentages, rates and weighted averages allows students to take on more subtle mathematical and statistical topics that are commonly found in the everyday media, such as:

- *Simpson's paradox*: Suppose that a city hospital has a higher death rate among patients than does a rural hospital. But when patients are classified as being in either good or fair condition, patients in each condition have a lower death rate at the city than at the rural hospital (Schield 2006b).

- *Standardization*: Standardization takes into account the influence of a confounder using algebra or a graphical technique. Given the average family income for white and black families by type of family (single parent vs. married couple) and given the percentage of married couple families in each race, what percentage of the U.S. black-white family income gap is explained by differences in family structure? (Schield 2006b).

- *Cases attributable*: In the U.S. in 2003, the poverty rate was 25% in single-parent homes (5% in married-family homes). There are 4.5 million single-parent homes. How many of the single-parent families in poverty are attributable to their being a single-parent family? (Schield 2004b).

- *Bayes comparison*: Men are 94% of those in prison but 49% of the U.S. population so men are almost twice as prevalent among those in prison as among those in the general population. Using Bayes rule, we can conclude that men are almost twice as likely to go to prison as are those in the general population (Schield 2004b).

Conclusion

In preparing students for four-year colleges, school mathematics educators must justify their choice of topics and pedagogy for the 40% of college students who will graduate in non-quantitative majors. Satisfying the needs of this group is critical. These students are more likely to become journalists, policy advocates, lawyers, opinion makers and political leaders, thereby influencing local and national policies. College students in non-quantitative majors need quantitative literacy—even if they cannot (and need not) solve a quadratic equation or factor a cubic expression.

Whenever possible, school mathematics educators should look for ways to use context (the quantitative elements of everyday life) to drive the choice of quantitative topics rather than selecting mathematical topics and then looking for contexts in which it is used. Mathematics educators should focus more on those mathematical topics that are encountered most often in everyday contexts and that teachers in all majors can understand and will expect of their students. "Mathematics in context" should focus less on going from mathematics to context and focus more on going from context to mathematics.

In short, describing, comparing and standardizing percentages, rates and averages in context—in graphs, in tables and in ordinary English statements—should be an important element in the "mathematics in context" curriculum for both primary and secondary school students.

Acknowledgements. Thanks to the anonymous Wingspread reviewers, Gail Burrill, former president of the NCTM, Dr. Jane Watson, Professor of Education at the University of Tasmania, Bernie Madison, founder of the National Numeracy Network, and Lynn Steen, former president of the MAA, for their suggestions. Thanks to the W. M. Keck Foundation for their support of the W. M. Keck Statistical Literacy Project at Augsburg College "to develop statistical literacy as an interdisciplinary curriculum in the liberal arts." Figures 2-6 were obtained from *USA Today On-Line Snapshots,* © USA TODAY, reprinted with permission.

References

Atkinson, M. & Wills, J. (2007). Table reading skills as quantitative literacy. Midwest Sociological Society, Chicago, IL.

Best, J. (2001). *Damned Lies and Statistics.* University of California Press.

Best, J. (2002). People Count: The Social Construction of Statistics. Augsburg College. See www.StatLit.org/pdf/2002BestAugsburg.pdf.

Best, J. (2004). *More Damned Lies and Statistics.* University of California Press.

Best, J. (2007). Including Construction in Quantitative Literacy. Midwest Sociological Society. See www.StatLit.org/pdf/2007BestMSS.pdf.

Briggs, W. L. (2006). What math should all college students know? In R. Gillman (Ed.), *Current practices in quantitative literacy* (pp. 17–19). Washington, DC: Mathematical Association of America.

Gillman, R. (Ed.). (2006). *Current Practices in Quantitative Literacy.* Washington, DC: Mathematical Association of America.

Isaacson, M. (2005). Statistical Literacy: An Online Course at Capella University. *Proceedings of the Joint Statistical Meetings* (pp. 2244–2252). Alexandria, VA: American Statistical Association. See www.StatLit.org/pdf/2005IsaacsonASA.pdf.

Isom, M. (2004). Sectional news at Arizona State University. MAA Southwestern Section Newsletter, Vol. 18, #4. See oak.ucc.nau.edu/hagood/MAASW/Newsletter047.htm

Lesser, L. (2001). Representations of reversal: Exploring Simpson's paradox. In A. A. Cuoco and F. R. Curcio (Eds.), *The roles of representation in school mathematics* (pp. 129–145). Reston, VA: National Council of Teachers of Mathematics. See www.StatLit.org/pdf/2001LesserNCTM.pdf.

Lutsky, N. (2006). Quirks of rhetoric: A quantitative analysis of quantitative reasoning in student writing. *Proceedings of the Joint Statistical Meetings* (pp. 2319–2322). Alexandria, VA: American Statistical Association. See www.StatLit.org/pdf/2006LutskyASA.pdf.

Lutzer, D. J., Maxwell, J. W., & Rodi, S. B. (2002). *Statistical Abstract of Undergraduate Programs in the Mathematical Sciences in the United States; Fall 2000 CBMS Survey.* Providence, RI: American Mathematical Society.

Madison, B. L. (2006). Pedagogical challenges of quantitative literacy. *Proceedings of the Joint Statistical Meetings* (pp. 2323–2328). Alexandria, VA: American Statistical Association. See www.StatLit.org/pdf/2006MadisonASA.pdf.

National Council of Teachers of Mathematics (2007). Mission statement. www.nctm.org/about/.

Schau, C. (2003). Students' attitudes: The "other" important outcome in statistics education. *Proceedings of the Joint Statistical Meetings* (pp. 3673–3681). Alexandria, VA: American Statistical Association. See www.StatLit.org/pdf/2003SchauASA.pdf.

Schield, M. (2004a). Statistical literacy and liberal education at Augsburg College. *Peer Review,* 6, 16–18. Draft at www.StatLit.org/pdf/2004SchieldAACU.pdf.

Schield, M. (2004b). Statistical literacy curriculum design. IASE Curriculum Design Roundtable. See www.StatLit.org/pdf/2004SchieldIASE.pdf.

Schield, M. (2006a). Statistical literacy survey analysis: Reading tables and graphs of rates and percentages. International Conference on Teaching Statistics. www.StatLit.org/pdf/2006SchieldICOTS.pdf.

Schield, M. (2006b). Presenting confounding and standardization graphically. STATS magazine, Fall 2006. Draft at www.StatLit.org/pdf/2006SchieldSTATS.pdf.

Schield, M. (2006c). Percentage graphs in *USA Today* snapshots online. *Proceedings of the Joint Statistical Meetings* (pp. 2364–2371). Alexandria, VA: American Statistical Association.

Schield, M. (2007a). Teaching the Social Construction of Statistics. Midwest Sociological Society. See www.StatLit.org/pdf/2007SchieldMSS.pdf.

Schield, M. (2007b). Statistical Literacy at Augsburg College: GST 200. Augsburg College. See www.StatLit.org/pdf/2007SchieldGST200.pdf.

Steen, L. (Ed.). (2001). *Mathematics and democracy: The case for quantitative literacy.* Princeton, NJ: National Council on Education and the Disciplines.

Terwilliger, J. and M. Schield (2004). *Frequency of Simpson's Paradox in NAEP Data.* American Educational Research Association. See www.StatLit.org/pdf/2004TerwilligerSchieldAERA.pdf.

TIMSS Study. (1999). Students' backgrounds and attitudes toward mathematics. Chapter 4 of *Mathematics benchmarking report—eighth grade.* Found at isc.bc.edu/timss1999b/mathbench_report/mathb_exhibits/T2R51110.html

U.S. Census Bureau (2006). *Statistical abstract of the United States: 2006* (125th edition). Washington, DC: Author.

U.S. Census Bureau (2007). *Statistical abstract of the United States: 2007* (126th edition). Washington DC: Author.

Wu, H. (2002). Elementary mathematics instruction: Chapter 2, fractions. math.berkeley.edu/~wu/

Preparing Students for the Business of the Real (and Highly Quantitative) World

Corrine Taylor[*]
Wellesley College

Could the half trillion dollar aggregate cost of the telecommunications crash of the 1990s and early 2000s have been mitigated had our nation's schools and colleges emphasized quantitative reasoning (applied math, logic, and statistics in context within a culture of spelling out and questioning assumptions) rather than "school mathematics" divorced from the real world?[1] Likely so. John Handley, telecommunications consultant and author of *Telebomb: The Truth Behind the $500-Billion Telecom Bust and What the Industry Must Do to Recover* describes myriad problems that precipitated the telecom crisis, beginning with false assumptions and faulty quantitative reasoning that resulted in tremendous overinvestment in communications networks. Explaining the "fundamental fallacy" Handley writes:

> To attract investors, new entrants [in the race to cover the US in fiber-optic cable] depended on a catch phrase that passed for fact at the time but has since been debunked. Beginning in 1997, various parties interested in seeing the Internet grow began repeatedly to drop the sound bite that "Internet traffic doubles every ninety days." Although

---
[*]Corrine Taylor is Director of the Quantitative Reasoning Program at Wellesley College. After graduating from the College of William and Mary in 1988, she worked as a strategic planning analyst for MetLife Auto & Home Insurance. In 1998 she received her Ph.D. in economics from the University of Wisconsin-Madison and joined the faculty in Wellesley's Department of Economics where she teaches courses in quantitative reasoning, statistics, microeconomics, public economics, and the economics of education. Her research focuses on elementary and secondary school finance. In 2001 she was appointed the first director of the College's QR Program and in 2007 became president of the National Numeracy Network. *E-mail*: ctaylor1@wellesley.edu.

this was probably true during the early commercialization of the Internet in 1995 and 1996, it should have been obvious that growth on that scale could not be sustained. It is much easier to grow at a given percentage from a smaller base. It is easier to grow revenue from $100 to $200 than it is to grow from $100,000,000 to $200,000,000, for example. An additional $100 is easier to find than $100,000,000.[2]

Handley goes on to say that "the sound bite persisted at a time when most entrepreneurs were moving too fast in the Internet land grab to spend time *thinking for themselves*"[3] (emphasis mine). In today's highly quantitative world, we need citizens who can think critically about such issues. This paper asks: How can we best prepare today's students who may be the entrepreneurs of the future—whether on the scale of investing millions in telecommunications or, more likely, investing in their own small businesses—with the quantitative skills and habits of mind to routinely question such assumptions and "do the math"? How can high school and college curricula offer more authentic opportunities for students to apply quantitative reasoning (QR) in business and personal finance arenas that they will likely encounter upon graduation? And how can we provide better training for teachers so that they can guide students in combining the important business (and general critical thinking) skills of seeking out information, analyzing that information, making decisions, and communicating findings? Moreover, how do we create a society of people who routinely *think for themselves* and not follow the mob even when—especially when—the real world problems at hand are quantitative in nature?

What skills matter most?

Quantitative reasoning skills are required of today's citizens in so many aspects of everyday life, as is emphasized in *Mathematics and Democracy: The Case for Quantitative Literacy*.[4] This paper focuses on one specific area: business. What kinds of QR skills are most important in the business world? To answer this question we draw from multiple sources. First, we examine the mathematics content areas and QR skills emphasized on the aptitude test generally required of candidates for masters' of business administration (MBA) programs. Second, we explore other QR skills and learning approaches that business schools value at both the undergraduate and graduate school levels. Third, we examine the skills that business consulting firms screen for when interviewing job applicants. Next we consider the quantitative business skills required in planning, launching, managing, and closing a small business. Assisting with the explorations above are the insights of experts from business schools, consulting firms, and the Small Business Administration. We also gain insights from some leaders in the QR movement and from my own experiences as a strategic planning analyst and as a college instructor for economics and QR.

Lessons from the GMAT, business schools, and the CLA

The GMAT (Graduate Management Admission Test) is the test used by more than 1,500 business schools world-wide to assess the potential of applicants to MBA programs.[5] This aptitude test has three main sections: the analytical writing section, the verbal section, and the quantitative section.[6] The assessment's emphasis on communication skills—particularly the importance of writing clearly about analytical topics—is noteworthy. The quantitative section uses two types of multiple-choice questions: (1) "problem solving questions" that are designed to test basic mathematics skills, the understanding of basic concepts, and the ability to reason and solve quantitative problems; and (2) "data sufficiency questions" that require one to examine a question and two statements that contain additional information and determine whether there is sufficient information to answer the question posed.[7] While the multiple choice format of the quantitative section is understandably disappointing to advocates of open-ended, authentic QR problems (and yet is the norm for standardized tests),[8] it is the *mathematics content areas*, not the format, of this test section that is of most interest in understanding what is required of business school applicants. Also of interest are the combinations of skills required in addressing these questions.

Calculus is *not* a content area tested on this assessment; rather the GMAT's quantitative section assesses one's core skills in arithmetic, algebra, and basic geometry. Most questions deal with the commonly applied skills of using basic arithmetic operations; dealing with fractions, percents, and ratios; reading and interpreting graphs; measuring and comparing values, often with different units; and working with models of linear and exponential growth. The data sufficiency questions test one's ability to reason in addition to being able to apply the mathematics content areas above. These emphases make sense given the most common applications in the major business disciplines of accounting, finance, marketing, and management. Indeed, Richard Cleary, Professor of Mathematical Sciences at Bentley College, reports that while calculus is important in a few specialized areas such as risk management, actuarial science, and high-end finance, and is helpful in solving economic problems of constrained optimization, the great majority of business problems do not involve calculus or other high-level mathematics; rather, most business problems utilize the mathematics content areas tested on the GMAT as well as statistics.[9]

These are precisely the areas that QR proponents argue should be emphasized more in context at both the high school and college level if we are to create a quantitatively literate society able to handle the business of the real world.[10]

Beyond knowing how to apply mathematics to solve problems in context, Cleary (along with every other business or economics professor I know) ranks the ability to "guess and check" as a key QR skill, especially given the common use of technology. That is, before beginning quantitative business problem— even a narrowly defined calculation problem—one ought to have an idea of the right order of magnitude of the solution; if one cannot even make a guess, then how clearly can one understand the problem? And on the other side, once a solution is determined to a problem, one ought to be able to check that it is of a reasonable value.[11] We all know stories of students who have used a calculator to perform a computation, made some error in pushing buttons, and proceeded to report an answer that was clearly unreasonable – way off in order of magnitude. Teachers worried that "calculator dependency" kept students from actual *thinking*. Now, with bigger, more complex business problems (problems that still use core skills, but often with large numbers of observations or repeated steps for many years of analysis), students routinely use computers as tools in their problem solving, creating a concern over "computer dependency." As Cleary says, "It's easy to use a very powerful computer to get a very wrong answer."[12] While business students need to know how to perform calculations and complex analyses on computers, more than ever, they need to apply core quantitative skills to estimate and check for the reasonableness of answers.

Many other quantitative reasoning skills are needed to address authentic business problems that are, by nature, complex. Real world problems require devising an overarching plan for addressing the problem, finding information, assessing the quality of the information, making reasonable assumptions where information is not readily available, determining the best analytical approach, using technology when needed to perform the appropriate analyses, checking the reasonableness of calculated values, interpreting the meaning of calculated values, evaluating the decisions that those values lead to, and communicating the findings clearly, both orally and in writing. Business applications naturally integrate these many critical thinking skills that are too often taught in isolation in most K–12 schools and even in colleges. Unfortunately, in mathematics courses, students are rarely asked to find data or make assumptions; textbook problems typically provide all the required information and one simply needs to use the technique *du jour* to combine the information given in order to produce the desired result. (Today is Tuesday, linear growth day, so I must be able to fit this problem into the formula $y = mx + b$.) Also, because mathematics courses tend to focus on the techniques used in making calculations, students are rarely asked to communicate their finding using complete sentences. At the same time, writing courses typically focus on literary analysis or on other topics in the humanities; most high school students (and even college students) get very little practice writing about quantitative topics outside of crafting science laboratory reports.

High schools and colleges would likely benefit from adopting the integrated learning approaches used by undergraduate business programs and graduate schools of business in honing students' quantitative skills and, more generally, their critical thinking skills. In particular, the case method, used extensively in business programs around the world, is an effective approach.[13] A case presents a "detailed account of a real-life business situation, describing the dilemma of the 'protagonist'—a real person with a real job who is confronted with a real problem."[14] Students are presented the situation "exactly as the protagonist saw it, including ambiguous evidence, shifting variables, imperfect knowledge, no obvious right answers, and a ticking clock that impatiently demands action."[15] In the case method, students are not merely charged with making a *calculation*; rather, they must make a *decision*: What should the protagonist do? With this approach, students cannot help but be motivated and engaged. Case studies are so much more interesting and relevant than the typical artificial little questions in most mathematics text books. At the same time they challenge students to apply what Benjamin Bloom calls "higher order thinking" skills, going beyond questions requiring *knowledge, comprehension,* and *application,* to those involving *analysis, synthesis,* and *evaluation.*[16] Because case studies require students to evaluate quantitative evidence, determine reasonable analytical approaches, perform complex calculations, make decisions, and communicate not only the results but also the process, they provide the opportunity for students to sharpen all their QR skills.

A relatively new assessment system (piloted in 2002) takes just such a holistic approach, using open-ended "performance tasks," among other instruments, to measure improvements in college students' critical thinking, analytical reasoning, problem solving, and writing.[17] The Collegiate Learning Assessment (CLA), developed by the Council for Aid to Education in conjunction with the RAND Corporation, provides formative assessments of the value-added at colleges and universities by testing a sample of each participating institution's first year students in the fall and seniors in the spring. The performance tasks completed by the students are authentic activities "such as preparing a memo or policy recommendation by using a series of documents that must be reviewed and evaluated" allowing the students to demonstrate their "ability to interpret, analyze, and synthesize information." The CLA tasks I have seen are excellent; I hope that these types of open-ended, holistic problems are used more often to assess QR skills in business and in other disciplines as well.

Lessons from consulting firms

Firms that help businesses of varying sizes grow and prosper by providing management and/or technology consulting hire both individuals with higher degrees such as MBAs and graduates straight out of college. College graduates may have bachelors' degrees in arts or sciences but need to exhibit strong critical thinking, analytical, writing, and oral communication skills, says Beth Reiland, Chief Personnel Officer for the Exeter Group.[18] Reiland argues that the kinds of core skills tested on the GMAT quantitative section are the necessary building blocks of problem-solving, but emphasizes that having these analytical skills is not sufficient. Workplaces need individuals who can *communicate effectively* with each other about quantitative issues. "In the business consulting environment, we come up with better solutions using collaborative thinking processes," Reiland explains. "Solutions to complex problems are improved by working in cooperative groups: sharing assumptions and information, thinking aloud about approaches, and testing ideas with others." Therefore, Reiland continues, educators need to "devote energies to developing a clear language for communicating about quantitative topics."[19]

The importance of being able to communicate effectively about quantitative topics is reflected in the personal interview process used by consulting firms today. In the old days, interviews were essentially chats about one's education and interests; today they are challenging tests of the applicant's analytical and communications skills. In *How Would You Move Mount Fuji? Microsoft's Cult of the Puzzle: How the World's Smartest Companies Select the Most Creative Thinkers*, author William Poundstone describes how loosely-defined questions and Fermi puzzles are being used in interviews of not only technology firms such as Microsoft, but also Fortune 500 companies, "law firms, banks, consulting firms, and the insurance industry; airlines, media, advertising, and even the armed forces."[20] Below are a few examples of these puzzles from Poundstone's book:

- How many gas stations are there in the United States?
- How long would it take to move Mount Fuji?
- Suppose you're hired as an IRS agent. Your first job is to find out whether a nanny agency is cheating on its taxes. How would you do it?[21]

Depending on the situation, the interviewer may expect the interviewee to be able to solve the problem without additional information, or he or she may be willing to provide more information when asked for specific details. For many of these puzzles the emphasis is on making reasonable assumptions, coming up with an approach for solving the problem, and applying QR skills to come up with what my boss used to call a "back-of-the-envelope" solution. Calculators are verboten. Typically the interviewer explains that he or she would like a "running monologue" (if not a dialogue) to show the interviewee's thought process.[22] The interviewer assesses not only the interviewee's overarching approach, logic, and mathematics skills, but also his or her exposition. Consulting firms do not want to hire mathematics geniuses who can solve problems on paper but cannot talk about the approaches and solutions with others. They want individuals who can communicate with others on a team about assumptions, techniques, results, and decisions.

In addition to, or instead of, presenting loosely-defined puzzles, many management consulting firms present interviewees with short cases similar to those used in MBA programs. The interviewer presents the basic challenge faced by the protagonist, along with selected evidence. Interviewees need to process the relevant information and ask specific questions to obtain additional data that they think would be relevant to the problem at hand. Case studies are definitely dialogues. McKinsey & Company, a premier global management consulting firm, tells applicants: "During the case study we look for evidence of your ability on a number of different dimensions – logical reasoning, creativity, quantitative skills, business judgment (not business knowledge), pragmatism, and an ability to structure problem solving."[23] Again, in showcasing these abilities, the interviewee needs not only the logic and mathematics skills but also strong communication skills about quantitative topics.

Lessons from small businesses

While graduates of top MBA programs and employees of management consulting firms are known for working with Fortune 500 firms and other large and medium-sized corporations, 98% of businesses are categorized as "small businesses" with fewer than 100 employees and 99.7% are businesses with fewer than 500 employees.[24] These firms include "mom and pop" convenience stores, greengrocers, florists, drycleaners, small retail shops, restaurants, neighborhood fitness centers, landscapers, professionals such as dentists, lawyers, and accountants who "hang out their shingles," Web site development companies and other small providers of computer services, small manufacturing and construction companies, and many, many other types of businesses. The Small Business Administration (SBA), the US governmental agency that assists small businesses, provides resources including a Web-based planner to help small business owners plan, start, and manage a business, and when the time comes, sell the business.[25] The "Small Business Planner" provides information and resources on each of the following topics:[26]

Plan your business	Start your business	Manage your business	Getting out
Get ready	Find a mentor	Lead	Plan your exit
Write a business plan	Finance start-up	Make decisions	Sell your business
	Buy a business	Manage employees	Transfer ownership
	Buy a franchise	Market and price	Liquidate assets
	Name your business	Market and sell	File bankruptcy
	Choose a structure	Understand fair practices	Close officially
	Protect your ideas	Pay taxes	
	Get licenses, permits	Get insurance	
	Pick a location	Handle legal concerns	
	Lease equipment	Forecast	
		Advocate, stay informed	
		Use technology	
		Finance growth	

Examining these business decisions, we note that about half of them are quantitative in nature. More detailed questions for these topics would include: What combination of drawing from savings and taking out loans makes the most sense in financing my start-up? Should I buy or lease my equipment? If I take out a start-up loan or if I lease equipment, which of the various timelines offered is best for my particular circumstances? How much insurance do I need to get and from whom will I get the best coverage for the price? What prices should I charge for my products and services to cover my costs, provide a suitable rate of return, and remain competitive in the marketplace? What do I predict sales will be one year from now? In considering the mathematics skills required in addressing these types of questions, we note again that calculus is not essential; rather, arithmetic, algebra, and statistics are the core mathematics content areas.

Of course, the real trick is not simply being able to solve an algebraic equation, but being able to translate the language of the real world business question into the relevant mathematics problem, finding the information needed to answer that problem, and understanding what the mathematical solution implies for the best decision. Small business owners need to be able to communicate with bankers, lawyers, tax consultants, their suppliers, their customers, their employees, and others about these many quantitative issues. Robert Berney, retired chief economist for the SBA, stresses that the K–12 foundations of clear communications in English (reading and writing) are every bit as essential as basic mathematics (arithmetic) in preparing students for the world of business.[27] Those famous "three Rs" are still the key to a solid base of critical thinking skills.

Lessons from QR teachers

William Briggs, co-author of *Using and Understanding Mathematics: A Quantitative Reasoning Approach* and Professor of Mathematics at the University of Colorado–Denver, gives an example of a very short, basic business problem he assigns his QR students. The problem is taken directly from a newspaper article: The CEO of a struggling airline plans to take an 85% salary cut. The cut would reduce his salary to $500,000 per year. What was his salary before the cut?[28] Of course, the problem is a simple algebra problem at its core, but the algebra itself is not the hard part for most students. Once the problem is in the form $x - 0.85x = \$500,000$, students find it pretty easy to solve for x. The real challenge for Brigg's college students is in translating the words into the algebraic expression. Students need more opportunities to work with practical word problems and they need practice developing the critical thinking strategies to do that translation from words into formulas. Briggs helps his college students develop these skills, having them first draw a picture then write a sentence such as "old salary minus 85% of old salary equals new salary of $500,000." These strategies need to be emphasized more when students first learn algebra.

Bernard Madison, Mathematics Professor at the University of Arkansas and first president of the National Numeracy Network, similarly notes that real world quantitative problems are "entangled in contexts that are often confusing, inexplicit, and incomplete. Once we untangle and clarify the quantitative content [within] these contexts, the mathematics or statistics may be elementary, but the contexts and reflection of our results back into the contexts are often sophisticated and complex."[29] To give his students practice working with quantitative analyses in authentic contexts, Madison has developed over a dozen case-like applications based on newspaper and magazine articles.[30] In my classes, too, students analyze data from various sources and claims in the media. I challenge my students to question headlines with astounding numbers. Exactly how was that value calculated? Is it reasonable? These applications of quantitative reasoning ripped from the headlines keep the students from being able to ask the dreaded question "When will I ever use this math?" Students see the relevance immediately and are actively engaged in the application of the logic, mathematics, and statistics. Presumably, such motivated students will learn the material, retain it, and be able to apply what they learned in other situations.

Summary of core QR skills needed in business

So what skills matter most in business? In terms of mathematics content areas, while calculus is undoubtedly important for high finance and some other specialty fields, the core areas of arithmetic, algebra, mathematical modeling (especially linear versus exponential growth), logic, and basic statistics are most often applied in the business world. Students need to work extensively with percents and ratios in real contexts. They need to develop a questioning mentality. They need to learn to estimate, to "guess and check" so they are not fooled by the black box of computer computations. It is practice with *applications* of the core mathematics skills that students need most. Learning to solve for *x* in an algebraic equation is a necessary but not sufficient condition for being able to solve a real world problem involving algebra. Students need practice with messy, loosely-defined problems in authentic contexts and need to tackle such problems from beginning to end. A complex, real-world problem requires formulating a multi-stepped plan for addressing the question, tracking down relevant information and making realistic assumptions, estimating the answer, performing required calculations (which often require the use of calculators or computers), evaluating the outcomes, and communicating the findings. Communications skills cannot be emphasized enough. Developing a language for communicating clearly about quantitative topics is essential. Skills in mathematics, logic, and statistics combined with the ability to question assumptions, plan approaches, and communicate findings are critical in the business world and in our quantitative world at large.

How can we help teachers prepare students for QR and the business world?

The lessons above provide important implications for the revitalization of teacher training and the improvement of curricula for students in K–12 schools and for undergraduate students in our nation's colleges and universities. To help students develop and retain the kinds of quantitative skills that they will apply in the real world, especially in business, we need to move away from a fragmented teaching and learning approach to a more holistic one. In particular, we need to offer more opportunities for students to make *decisions* that involve information-gathering and assessment, quantitative analyses, and communications about quantitative topics, not merely textbook *calculations* that use mathematics. Schools still need to teach English and mathematics, and separately at times, but then they also need to help students combine their research, mathematics, logic, reading and writing skills in various contexts—be it in a physics, chemistry, or biology laboratory or in a history, social studies, or economics class. In short, schools must not only teach mathematics; they must also provide opportunities to practice quantitative reasoning. The differences between the two are characterized in Bernard Madison's table below.[31]

Mathematics	Quantitative Reasoning
Power in abstraction	Real, authentic contexts
Power in generality	Specific, particular applications
Some context dependency	Heavy context dependency
Society independent	Society dependent
Apolitical	Political
Methods and algorithms	Ad hoc methods
Well-defined problems	Ill-defined problems
Approximation	Estimation is critical
Heavily disciplinary	Interdisciplinary
Problem solutions	Problem descriptions
Few opportunities to practice outside the classroom	Many practice opportunities outside the classroom
Predictable	Unpredictable

What needs to happen for teachers to routinely provide such QR opportunities for their students? First we need mathematics teachers to become well-versed in authentic mathematics applications from a variety of disciplines. Such applications may come from the sciences, the social sciences, and even the arts. Personal finance and business applications may be particularly useful in applied mathematics courses. Additionally, mathematics teachers need to become comfortable assigning and grading writings on quantitative topics. These assignments can start small: "Write a sentence that explains your results in context" or "Write a paragraph describing the graph you created." Mathematics teachers also need to rely less on artificial text book problems and assign more loosely-defined problems such as Fermi puzzles and case studies—not full-blown HBS cases but real world problems from newspapers, magazines, and journals. Responsibility for developing students' QR skills cannot be placed in the hands of mathematics teachers alone, however. Teachers in quantitative disciplines and in English classes need to jump on the QR bandwagon, as well. Social studies and science teachers, for example, might be challenged to assign more papers requiring students to describe supporting tables and graphs. Writing teachers might move toward more assignments requiring the presentation of quantitative evidence. And teachers in quantitative disciplines need to be patient enough to remind students of the mathematics, logic, and statistics needed to be combined in new applications in their subject areas.

To help teachers stretch in these ways, teacher education programs and in-service training programs need to provide more interdisciplinary opportunities. While training at the elementary school level tends to do this, secondary school training becomes much more discipline specific. The only way to get students to combine their information literacy, mathematics, and communications skills within various contexts is to train teachers to do the same. Teachers of mathematics and a variety of quantitative disciplines might benefit from courses in the case study method or project-based learning. These methods naturally require one to work in teams, enhancing problem-solving and communication skills. Workshops specifically designed to offer teachers examples of good interdisciplinary QR projects might also be offered to teachers. I taught such a week-long summer workshop last year to secondary school mathematics teachers in Virginia. Those workshop attendees expressed a strong desire for more curricular materials that they could easily use in their classrooms.

K–12 teachers have so many demands on their time that they do not always have the time to create interesting QR exercises from articles in last Sunday's *New York Times*. If states become more explicit about student expectations in quantitative reasoning rather than in mathematics *per se* (on their standards of learning and standardized assessments, for example) then perhaps publishers will recognize the demand for more authentic QR exercises and will provide such resources for teachers. Such resources already exist at the elementary school level. For example, TERC, a non-profit education research and development organization dedicated to improving teaching and learning in math, science, and technology, offers the *Investigations in Number, Data, and Space* curricular materials. These "activity-based investigations encourage students to think creatively, develop their own problem-solving strategies, and work cooperatively. Students write, draw, and talk about math, as well as use manipulatives, calculators, and computers."[32] Similar multidisciplinary, activity-based materials need to be offered for secondary schools as well, where, as mentioned earlier, the tendency, unfortunately, is for schools to fragment the learning into distinct disciplines.

In colleges, as well, collaborative efforts to develop students' QR skills need to be encouraged. Team-teaching seminars or courses on quantitative, interdisciplinary topics might be helpful. I recently had the pleasure of team-teaching a new course in statistics in the biological sciences. I have not had biology since 9th grade but I know a good deal about teaching statistics and my co-teacher had never before taught statistics but is an expert in ecology and has done many statistical analyses in his biology research. Developing and teaching this course was an excellent opportunity for each of us to expand our own QR skills in new directions and our enthusiasm apparently carried over to our students, who reported gaining a great deal from this class. I can envision many other collaborative efforts that would allow students additional opportunities to develop QR skills that will help them throughout life. To succeed in business, students need to develop those "habits of mind" of questioning quantitative evidence, analyzing problems, and communicating about quantitative topics. The applications need not come directly from the world of business; they can be from a biology or history course or the front page of the newspaper.

Conclusion

To best prepare students for the highly quantitative real world of business, teachers need help in creating authentic, complex problems that integrate math, research, technology, and communication skills. Students need interesting and practical examples to make it abundantly clear that mathematics skills are applicable in the real world. Students need to be able to find information or make assumptions for "messy problems," plan a reasonable approach to a problem, apply mathematical techniques, check for the reasonableness of the answer, and communicate the findings including decisions. Students need to develop a questioning mentality.

Back to the *Telebomb* example, we would like to ensure that upon hearing of the "half trillion dollar aggregate cost" of the telecommunications bust that people would immediately question where that figure came from. Over how many years was that cost accrued? Over what geographical space? Just the US or the world? Exactly what costs were included and why? This number sure sounds big—is it really? Relative to what? When our nation's schools and colleges produce citizens who routinely question such headlines and ask those types of quantitative questions then we will have a population that is not only prepared for the business world but is prepared for the myriad quantitative issues of everyday life.

References

Bloom, B. S. (Editor). (1956). *Taxonomy of Educational Objectives, Handbook I: The Cognitive Domain*. New York, NY: David McKay Co, Inc.

Briggs, W. (2007, April 28). Teaching a quantitative literacy course. Keynote address presented at the Northeast Consortium on Quantitative Literacy's annual meeting, Vassar College.

Collegiate Learning Assessment Project. (n.d.). About CLA. Retrieved August 20, 2007, from www.cae.org/content/pro_collegiate.htm

Graduate Management Admission Council. (n.d.). Overview about us. Retrieved March 20, 2007, from www.gmac.com/gmac/aboutus/

Graduate Management Admission Council. (n.d.) GMAT overview. Retrieved March 20, 2007, from www.mba.com/mba/TaketheGMAT/TheEssentials/ WhatIstheGMAT/ GMATOverviewNEW.htm

Graduate Management Admission Council. (n.d.) Quantitative section. Retrieved March 20, 2007, from www.mba.com/mba/TaketheGMAT/TheEssentials/ WhatIstheGMAT/ GMATOverviewNEW.htm

Handley, J. (2005). *Telebomb: the truth behind the $500-billion telecom bust and what the industry must do to recover*. New York, NY: AMACOM, American Management Association.

Harvard Business School. (n.d.) The case method. Retrieved April 20, 2007, from www.hbs.edu/case/

Madison, B. (2005, May). What is a course in QL? In *Newsletter of the National Numeracy Network*. Retrieved April 20, 2007, from www.math.dartmouth.edu/~nnn/newsletter/001/

Madison, B. (2006, April 29). Assessment and QL: double trouble. Keynote address presented at the Northeast Consortium on Quantitative Literacy's annual meeting, Amherst College.

McKinsey & Co. (n.d.) Interview preparation. Retrieved March 27, 2007 from www.mckinsey.com/aboutus/careers/applyingtomckinsey/interviewing/index.asp

Poundstone, W. (2003). *How to move Mount Fuji? Microsoft's cult of the puzzle: how the world's smartest companies select the most creative thinkers*. New York, NY: Little, Brown and Company.

Schoenfeld, A. H. (2001). Reflections on an impoverished education. In L. A. Steen (Ed.) *Mathematics and democracy: the case for quantitative literacy* (pp. 49–54). Princeton, NJ: National Council on Education and the Disciplines.

Small Business Administration, Office of Advocacy. (n.d.) Employer firms, establishments, employment, and annual payroll; small firm size classes, 2004. Retrieved May 11, 2007, from www.sba.gov/advo/research/us_04ss.pdf

Small Business Administration. (n.d.). Small Business Planner. Retrieved March 20, 2007, from www.sba.gov/smallbusinessplanner/index.html

Stanford University, Graduate School of Business. (n.d.). Learning methods. Retrieved April 20, 2007, from www.gsb.stanford.edu/mba/academics/learning_methods.html

Steen, L. A. (Editor). (2001). *Mathematics and democracy: the case for quantitative literacy*. Princeton, NJ: National Council on Education and the Disciplines.

Steen, L. A. and the Design Team. (2001). The case for quantitative literacy. In L. A. Steen (Ed.) *Mathematics and democracy: the case for quantitative literacy* (pp. 1–22). Princeton, NJ: National Council on Education and the Disciplines.

TERC. (n.d.). Investigations in number, data, and space. Retrieved May 2, 2007, from www.terc.edu/work/440.html. TERC began in 1965 as the Technical Education Research Centers.

Endnotes

[1] For an excellent discussion of the difference between what Alan H. Schoenfeld describes as "school mathematics" and what is known as "quantitative literacy" or "quantitative reasoning" see *Mathematics and Democracy: The Case for Quantitative Literacy* prepared by the National Council on Education and the Disciplines, especially the case (the first chapter) by Lynn Steen and the Design Team and Schoenfeld's essay "Reflections on an Impoverished Education."

[2] Handley, p. 64.

[3] *Ibid.*

[4] See pp. 9–15 of the first chapter of Mathematics and Democracy for examples of the many ways that QR skills are needed in citizenship, medical decision making, and personal finance.

[5] This figure is from the Graduate Management Admission Council, the organization that provides the GMAT. For more about this organization, see www.gmac.com/gmac/aboutus/.

[6] For more details on each section of the GMAT, see www.mba.com/mba/TaketheGMAT/TheEssentials/WhatIstheGMAT/GMATOverviewNEW.htm.

[7] For more details on these two kinds of quantitative problems, see www.mba.com/mba/TaketheGMAT/TheEssentials/WhatIstheGMAT/QuantitativeSectionNEW.htm.

[8] Now that the GMAT, like many other standardized tests, is administered on line, it will be interesting to see whether future versions of the test move away from "multiple-guess" problems toward open ended questions. The relatively new Collegiate Learning Assessment, with its open-ended performance tasks, is discussed later in this paper.

[9] Personal communication with Richard Cleary, April 21, 2007. Bentley College in Waltham, MA offers both undergraduate and graduate business programs.

[10] See the "elements" of quantitative literacy, pp. 7–9 in "The Case for Quantitative Literacy," the first chapter of *Mathematics and Democracy*.

[11] Personal communication with Richard Cleary, April 21, 2007.

[12] *Ibid.*

[13] The case method was pioneered at Harvard Business School (HBS) in the 1920s and today more than 80% of HBS classes are built on this method, according to the school's Web site. www.hbs.edu/case. Other highly ranked business programs, such as Stanford's Graduate School of Business, also use case studies to a high degree, but more often employ other teaching methods including simulations, discussions, problem-solving sessions, role-plays, etc. www.gsb.stanford.edu/mba/academics/learning_methods.html.

[14] From www.hbs.edu/case/hbs-case.html.

[15] *Ibid.*

[16] The six categories of questions listed are commonly known as Bloom's Taxonomy, from Bloom *et al.*, 1956.

[17] This section is taken from the homepage of the Collegiate Learning Assessment (CLA) Project, at www.cae.org/content/pro_collegiate.htm.

[18] Personal communication with Beth Reiland, March 27, 2007. The Exeter Group is a technology consulting firm in Cambridge, MA.

[19] Personal communication with Beth Reiland, March 27, 2007.

[20] Page 7, *How Would You Move Mount Fuji?*

[21] Pages 81–82. These are just three of about 40 questions presented along with reasonable approaches to answering the questions in Poundstone's book.

[22] Poundstone offers more detailed tips on how to approach these kinds of interview problems in chapter 8.

[23] Much more detail about McKinsey's interviews can be found at www.mckinsey.com/aboutus/careers/applyingtomckinsey/interviewing/index.asp.

[24] Calculation based on data on the employment size of firms from the Small Business Administration's Office of Advocacy, www.sba.gov/advo/research/us_04ss.pdf.

[25] See the "Small Business Planner" at www.sba.gov/smallbusinessplanner/index.html.

[26] *Ibid.*

[27] Personal communication with Robert Berney, formerly of the SBA, March 20, 2007.

[28] William Briggs's presentation at the Northeast Consortium on Quantitative Literacy's annual meeting, Vassar College, April 28, 2007.

[29] From "What is a course in QL," by Bernard Madison, in the National Numeracy Network's May 2005 Newsletter.

[30] E-mail communication with Bernard Madison, May 2, 2007.

[31] Bernard Madison's presentation at the Northeast Consortium on Quantitative Literacy's annual meeting, Amherst College, April 29. 2006.

[32] For more on the TERC Investigations curriculum see www.terc.edu/work/440.html. TERC began in 1965 as the Technical Education Research Centers, but is known now as TERC.

Beyond Calculation: Quantitative Literacy and Critical Thinking about Public Issues

Joel Best[*]

University of Delaware

Calls for quantitative literacy tend to focus on matters of calculation, on improving students' abilities to understand mathematical operations and to employ them in practical circumstances. In this paper I argue that quantitative literacy needs to move beyond calculation to understand the social processes that shape the creation and consumption of statistics about public issues. In particular, I examine the nature of the social construction of statistics and discuss how such considerations might be used in teaching quantitative literacy.

Not surprisingly, many of the calls for improving quantitative literacy tend to come from those who teach mathematics. This is important, because mathematics classes center on what I will call *calculation*. I do not use this word as a mathematician might, in a narrow, technical sense; rather, I intend it to encompass all of the practices by which mathematical problems are framed and then solved. Thus, in my view, both someone adding up a column of figures and someone solving an abstract problem through a series of equations are engaged in forms of mathematical reasoning that I am calling calculation. People teach mathematics—and, for the most part, presume that they should teach it—as a series of increasingly complicated forms of calculation. Thus, mathematics instruction is a long march through ever more sophisticated tech-

---

[*]Joel Best is Professor of Sociology and Criminal Justice at the University of Delaware. In addition to *Damned Lies and Statistics* (2001) and *More Damned Lies and Statistics* (2004), his books include *Threatened Children* (1990), *Random Violence* (1999), *Flavor of the Month* (2006), and *Social Problems* (2008). He is a past president of the Society for the Study of Social Problems and the Midwest Sociological Society, a former editor of the journal *Social Problems*, and editor-in-chief of the new electronic journal *Sociology Compass*.

niques for framing and solving problems: that is, we first learn to count, then to add, etc., etc., until different individuals top out at algebra, trigonometry, calculus, or whatever.

Because mathematics instruction is organized around principles of calculation, calls for quantitative literacy tend to assume that students are not sufficiently adept as calculators, and that they need to improve their calculating skills, that they either need to beef up their abilities to carry out more sophisticated calculations, or that they need to become better at recognizing how to apply their abstract calculation skills to real-world situations. I do not doubt that both sort of improvements are needed, but this paper argues that key forms of quantitative literacy require moving beyond calculation.

It will already be obvious that I am not a mathematician. I am a sociologist, interested in how and why particular social problems emerge as public issues—why is it that one year public concern focuses on, say, the health risks of breast implants, and then, a few years later, attention shifts to road rage or identity theft. I have written about the role that statistics play in this process, the ways that people use numbers to convince one another that this or that is a big problem (Best, 2001, 2004). Thinking critically about such statistics requires considering both the way those numbers are calculated and the processes by which they are socially constructed. My goal in this paper is to argue that teaching quantitative literacy requires that we confront issues of *construction*, as well as calculation.

What Does It Mean to Say that Numbers Are Socially Constructed?

The term *social construction* attracted faddish attention in recent academic cultural wars; it was invoked as a justification for various relativistic, postmodern positions taken by critical literary theorists, and denounced by those who saw themselves as defending objectivity and science (Boghossian, 2006; Hacking, 1999). Forget all that. The concept of social construction originated in sociology (Berger & Luckmann, 1966), and I will use the term in its narrower, sociological sense.

Humans depend upon language to understand the world, and language is a social phenomenon. We learn language from other people, and that means that all of the meanings we ascribe to the world are understood through those people's—their language's—categories. In this sense, all knowledge is socially constructed.

In particular, numbers are social constructions. Numbers do not exist in nature. Every number is a product of human activity: somebody had to do the calculations that produced that figure. Somebody had to decide what to count, and how to go about counting. This is not a mundane observation, at least when we encounter numbers about public issues. Understanding those figures requires, not just that we comprehend the calculations that produced them, but also that we appreciate the process of social construction.

Statistics and Public Issues

Let me begin with some examples of the sorts of numbers that regularly appear in discussions of public issues. When activists try to raise concern about some neglected social problem, when the media cover public issues, when political leaders propose new policies to address some concern—these are all occasions when statistics are likely to be invoked:

- Very often, when people seek to draw attention to some social problem, they offer numeric estimates for the extent of the phenomenon. Usually, these figures support claims that this is a big problem, one that demands attention (e.g., there are two million missing children each year; or one billion birds die annually in the U.S. from flying into windows).

- Polling data is used to describe the public's views about some social issue. Advocates often use such poll results to suggest that there is broad support for their causes (e.g., pro-life activists argue that most Americans are opposed to most abortions, whereas pro-choice advocates insist that the vast majority of Americans oppose ending legal abortion; similarly, both those favoring and opposed to adopting voucher systems for education point to surveys indicating that a majority of the public supports their position).

- Government agencies release statistical indicators (e.g., the crime rate, the unemployment rate, the poverty rate) that track conditions in the U.S. (e.g., in 2006, the U.S. Fish and Wildlife Service reported that total wetlands acreage increased between 1998 and 2004; earlier in 2007, the Census Bureau announced that racial and ethnic minorities now account for one-third of the nation's population).

- Rarely does a week go by without the news media summarizing some new medical research relating to the incidence of various medical problems (e.g., "1 in 5 Students Practice Self-Injury") or lifestyle risks (e.g., eating particular foods, smoking, or drinking alcohol increases or decreases the risks of particular health problems).

Such statistics are intended, not just to inform people, but to shape their attitudes and behaviors. Claims that millions of people are affected by some social problem can generate widespread concern: thus, claims in the 1980s that there were millions of missing children led to Congress passing new laws, many parents voluntarily having their children fingerprinted, and countless milk cartons displaying blurry pictures of missing kids. Arguments that most people hold particular opinions encourage other people to adopt those views. And stories about dramatic medical breakthroughs can inspire people to change their lifestyles (remember the oat-bran craze?).

However, many of these numbers can not bear close inspection. Particularly when people are first drawing attention to social problems, it is unlikely that anyone can do much more than guess about how many people—let alone birds—might be affected. The very fact that advocates on opposing sides of the abortion and school-voucher debates insist that most Americans sympathize with their positions suggests that their statistics—or at least the impressions they convey—must be flawed. And contradictory news reports that a particular food or beverage is bad—or is it good?—for one's health provide fodder for stand-up comedians' suggestions that scientists may not know what they are talking about.

Or take the recent fuss after the Centers for Disease Control and Prevention (CDC) declared that obesity killed 400,000 Americans in 2003, and warned that the obesity epidemic would soon surpass smoking as the leading cause of preventable deaths. This was followed, about a year later, by a report authored by a different set of CDC scientists that argued that 26,000 would be a more accurate figure for obesity deaths. The realization that public health experts, working at the same federal agency, could not agree on even a ballpark figure for obesity deaths generated a lot of head-scratching, head-shaking commentary in newspaper editorials.

Obviously, we live in a big, complicated world, and it is next to impossible to understand what is going on in that world without resorting to numbers that promise quantitative measures—there are this many, it is increased by this much, and so on. We encounter such numbers every day. They help shape our sense of what is right and wrong with our world. These are not numbers that we calculate, rather, they are figures that we consume. They are calculated and circulated by others, who bring them to our attention in order to inform or influence our thinking.

In my view, students need to learn to think critically about these numbers, and this requires more than having a sense of how those numbers were calculated. Students also need to understand these statistics as the results of social and political, as well as mathematical, processes. And this requires confronting matters of construction.

The Rhetorical Uses of Social Statistics

To begin, we need to appreciate that many of the numbers used to portray social issues are invoked for rhetorical effect. There is a marketplace for social problems, one in which advocates for many different causes compete to first capture public attention, and then convince people to take action. This competition occurs in many arenas: a newspaper's front page can only contain so many stories; a congressional committee can hold a limited number of hearings; and so on (Hilgartner & Bosk, 1988). If one problem surges to the forefront of public attention, others will be shoved aside.

Surviving this competition requires using compelling rhetoric, claims that seem surprising, disturbing, or otherwise worthy of attention. Statistics become one element in making persuasive claims. An arresting number can attract attention. And this, in turn, encourages advocates to use figures that will make their causes seem compelling. They want statistics that can get an issue media coverage, that can arouse members of the public to join the cause, that can force politicians to take action.

This need not be a cynical process; the point is not that these advocates are lying. To be sure, there may be occasions when people deliberately fabricate data, or when they intentionally use deceptive practices. But this sort of dishonesty probably cannot account for most—let alone all—of the dubious numbers presented about public issues. Advocates are often quite sincere: they believe they have identified what is in fact a big problem that has been shamefully neglected. It is therefore often easy for them to uncritically presume that their big number—which they may acknowledge is not much more than an educated guess—must be more-or-less accurate. But sincerity is no guarantee of accuracy. There have been heavily publicized numeric estimates for social problems that proved to be off by one, two, even three orders of magnitude.

Similarly, because apparently minor differences in how survey questions are worded can lead to very different results, it is often possible for advocates on opposing sides of an issue to argue that public opinion supports their position. Again, this need not be a cynical ploy, although when advocates report the results of polls they commissioned, their claims warrant especially careful examination. Still, people who hold strong views often spend a lot of time talking to others who share their concerns; it is easy for them to become convinced that—yes—most people agree with them.

Advocates become invested in their causes. This is by no means limited to having a financial interest in an issue's outcome; they may also stand to gain or lose influence and social status, depending upon what happens. Often, too, they come to have an emotional stake in their claims. If an "obesity epidemic" poses a serious threat to the nation's health, then the CDC and other public health officials—to say nothing of pharmaceutical manufacturers and other firms that sell weight-loss products—stand to gain (Oliver 2006). We should not be too quick to assume that the competing estimates for obesity-related deaths emanating from CDC simply reflect different calculation choices; the agency's leadership has a considerable stake in maximizing concern about the obesity threat.

The media also compete in the social problems marketplace. Their preference for important, dramatic stories means that they are drawn to claims that seem to present evidence for surprising conclusions (Two million children go missing each year! Research shows that eating oatmeal can cut your risk of heart disease!). Moreover, they are not under much obligation to check the numbers they report. So long as some researchers report that oat bran reduces health risks, a story about that research is accurate, regardless of whether oat bran actually has the beneficial effects claimed. Like advocates for competing causes, politicians, and even researchers, the media stand to benefit by promoting the sorts of large, compelling numbers that they consider newsworthy.

Of course it helps that many of the advocates estimating the scope of social problems, like many of those in the media reporting on those estimates, have problems with innumeracy (Paulos, 1988). They may want to promote accurate numbers, they may even believe that their numbers are accurate, yet they also may have trouble assessing accuracy, so that—even with the best intentions—badly flawed numbers get into circulation. Many people seem to subscribe to the innumerate notion that all big numbers are essentially equal ("A million, a billion—hey, they're all big numbers, what's the difference?"). Further, there is a widespread tendency to equate numbers with facts. Once a figure has attracted public attention, people feel free to repeat it. After all, a number suggests that somebody must have counted something—it must be true.

What about Authoritative Numbers?

It is, of course, easy to have doubts about statistics promoted by interested parties. The tobacco industry's critiques of research on the link between smoking and disease stand as a model of self-serving statistical hocus-pocus, and we can suspect that corporations generally will put forward numbers consistent with their interests. Similarly, we should anticipate that activists engaged in promoting various political and social causes will tend to use figures that advance their views. And there are many claims and counterclaims that this or that media outlet is "biased" and guilty of selective coverage. When I warn that statistics are socially constructed, these sorts of questionable sources for numbers may be the first thing that comes to mind.

But social construction can shape statistics in many other ways. To repeat: we need to consider how processes of social construction shape all statistics. Even apparently authoritative, objective figures need to be approached with care. Consider two examples involving problematic statistics produced by authoritative sources: the first a report summarizing the findings of an exhaustive, technically sophisticated government survey, the other a research report published in a major medical journal.

On March 30, 2006, Secretary of the Interior Gale Norton released a Fish and Wildlife Service report showing "a net gain in America's ... wetlands for the first time since the Service began compiling data in 1954." Secretary Norton was quoted as saying: "This report, prepared as part of President Bush's initiative to stem the loss of wetlands, is good news.... Although the overall state of our wetlands in still precarious, this report suggests that nationwide efforts to curb losses and restore wetlands habitats are on the right track" ("Secretaries Norton and Johanns," 2006, p. 1). This report quickly attracted criticism from conservationists, who pointed out that the apparent increase was due solely to the adoption of a new, more generous definition of wetlands, one that included golf-course water hazards and other man-made water areas (Barringer, 2006). (The report showed that acreage covered by swamps, marshes, and other natural wetlands had actually declined, and carefully noted that "This report does not assess the quality or condition of the nation's wetlands" (Dahl, 2006, p. 15).)

This example raises at least three sorts of interpretative questions. The first involves matters of technical calculation (the application of sophisticated technologies such as aerial and satellite imagery, geospatial analysis, and computerized mapping to measure areas defined as wetlands). The report discusses these methods in some detail. The second seems to straddle the boundary between calculation and construction: What should count as wetlands? Clearly, it is possible to disagree about the appropriate definition, as evidenced by the debate between the Administration and its environmentalist critics, although of Secretary Norton's readiness to claim that total wetlands acreage had increased, while ignoring the fact that the change was wholly due to redefining what counted, seems pretty shifty. Meanwhile, the third moves completely outside the domain of mathematical calculation: Why was the definition changed? Was the Bush Administration deliberately trying to use the broader definition of wetlands to conceal ongoing environmental degradation? Or is there some more innocent explanation? Understanding the change in wetlands acreage requires thinking critically about more than matters of pure calculation.

Or take a second example, also from 2006, when an article published in the journal *Pediatrics* attracted a good deal of press coverage. CNN.com

("Study: 1 in 5," 2006), for instance, used the headline: "Study: 1 in 5 Students Practice Self-Injury." Researchers (Whitlock, Eckenrode, & Silverman, 2006) invited 8,300 randomly selected students at two Ivy League universities to participate in an Internet-based survey; they received 2,875 usable responses (a 34.6 percent response rate). Of the respondents, 490 (17%—rounded up to one in five in many news stories, although the percentage is, of course, closer to one in six) reported having practiced some sort self-injurious behavior (SIB). The most common SIB was "severely scratched or pinched with fingernails or objects to the point that bleeding occurred or marks remained on the skin" (Whitlock, Eckenrode, & Silverman, 2006, p. 1943). Only 46 (i.e., 9.4 percent of those reporting SIB, which is to say 1.6 percent of the respondents) reported having inflicted an injury severe enough that it "should have been treated by a medical professional."

This study—and the resulting media coverage—offer a nice example of what happens when medical journals issue press releases (Shell, 1998). Journals presumably hope to raise their public standing by drawing attention to the important work published in their pages. Knowing that the press is unlikely to browse through each new issue without prompting, they issue news releases heralding newsworthy articles. This encourages accentuating the most striking aspects of the research (for instance, highlighting—even exaggerating—the substantial fraction of students practicing any sort of SIB, rather than drawing attention to the tiny percentage inflicting serious injuries). We might further suspect that an editor's decision to publish or reject a paper might sometimes be affected by the work's perceived potential for attracting media coverage. Once again, calculation is not at issue; however, interpreting the statistic presented in the media requires understanding something about the social process by which numbers find their way into our daily newspaper.

These examples remind us that government agencies, researchers, editors of scholarly journals, and other authorities have agendas, too. If obesity can be recognized as a huge public-health hazard, then the CDC can reasonably request more funding to deal with this problem. Even the most professional researchers would like to see their work appear in the best journals, and receive attention in the popular media. Such considerations can easily affect choices among ways of calculating and presenting data, so as to make the results seem as important or interesting—as competitive—as possible.

Implications for Teaching Quantitative Literacy

All of this has significant implications for teaching quantitative literacy. Evaluating the sorts of numbers—and the claims that such numeric evidence is used to support—that appear in news reports about public issues requires a broader set of critical thinking skills than mastering calculation. It also requires understanding something about the social construction of social statistics—about competition among advocates for different public issues, about the rhetorical role statistics can play in supporting advocates' claims, about the ways numbers are produced, about the assumptions and methods required to reach those numbers, about the limitations inherent in these processes, about the likely motivations and possible biases of the people who generate numbers, about ways the media make decisions to report or ignore numbers. That is, if quantitative literacy refers to a set of skills that can allow people to comfortably understand and critically examine the numbers they will encounter in their lives, including, in particular, figures that appear in discussions of public issues, then quantitative literacy instruction needs to extend beyond matters of calculation, to also encompass issues of construction.

The quantitative literacy movement seems to be composed largely of mathematicians and mathematics educators who have become skeptical about the practical value of traditional math instruction. They seem to view themselves—and are probably viewed by many mainstream mathematicians—as renegades who have ventured well outside the realm of what mathematicians recognize as mathematics. My point is that they have not gone far enough; that quantitative literacy requires some distinctly non-mathematical—that is, more than calculation-based—skills.

Because mathematics instruction emphases calculation, when it does introduce critical thinking, it tends to do so in a half-hearted, limited fashion. For example, statistics courses may make brief, tangential references to the problem of "bias." This is a convenient term, because it is ambiguous. On the one hand, statisticians use "bias" as part of the vocabulary of calculation: a sample drawn in some less than random manner is considered "biased"—what we might consider a technical, mathematical use of the term. But statistics teachers also may warn their students that some people with, say, an ideological agenda—a "bias"—may deliberately choose samples, word survey questions, or use other techniques to insure the sorts of results they favor. Thus, having an ideological bias becomes simply another form of bias in the mathematical sense. While this does offer a way of fitting ideology (and other social factors) within a mathematical framework (in that both sorts of bias skew the results of calculations), it does not go very far in preparing students to think critically about numbers, beyond offering an vague injunction to watch out for sources of bias.

While I am ill-qualified to advise primary, middle-school, and secondary educators on how to teach, let me offer one example of the sorts of lessons that might bring construction into the quantitative literacy classroom. When I teach social problems to lower-division college students, I give a couple people a brief homework assignment. One is to locate information from pro-life sources about surveys of Americans' attitudes toward abortion; the other, of course, is to do the same thing using pro-choice sources. They invariably come to the next class armed with contradictory claims that most Americans support the position of their respective groups. This engenders a nice discussion about the ways pollsters measure abortion attitudes, about alternative ways different people can interpret the same data, and so on.

I can imagine many similar ways to get students thinking critically about social statistics. The Census Bureau announces that nonwhite minorities now make up a third of the U.S. population. What does that mean? Does it matter that a substantial share of those being counted as minorities consider themselves white? What accounts for the bureau's eagerness to reclassify people formerly considered white as minorities? A typical newspaper front page contains social, economic, or political statistics that offers similar fodder for quantitative literacy lessons that incorporate matters of both calculation and construction.

But Will It Work?

In short, I envision quantitative literacy as going beyond calculation. However, I realize that, even if others find my argument convincing, it is likely to prove very difficult to incorporate this goal in quantitative literacy programs, because the people who teach math—who are, after all, the folks most interested in quantitative literacy, and the ones who will doubtless wind up teaching this material—have been trained to teach calculation, and they tend to define the problem of quantitative literacy in terms of people being insufficiently adept at calculation. They are likely to see the sorts of issues I have raising as, at most, peripheral to increasing quantitative literacy.

Ideally, of course, critical thinking lessons ought to be taught across the curriculum. We can imagine quantitative literacy lessons being taught in all sorts of classes. Couldn't students learn how to read—and ask questions about— say, news reports about new medical findings in science classes, or health classes, or social studies classes? Certainly this would be desirable, but getting the cause of quantitative literacy to spread beyond math classrooms obviously poses its own challenges. Those teaching other subjects will want to focus on what they see as the important content in their own subjects; they may doubt their qualifications or ability to venture into mathematical terrain; they may insist that teaching quantitative literacy is the job of math teachers; and so on.

In short, it seems to me the cause of quantitative literacy faces two challenges: first, recognizing that quantitative literacy must encompass more than matters of calculation; and, second, finding ways to integrate quantitative literacy—and critical thinking more generally—into the curriculum.

References

Barringer, F. (2006, March 31). Few marshes + more manmade ponds = increased wetlands. *New York Times*, p 16.

Berger, P. L., & Luckmann, T. (1966). *The social construction of reality: A treatise in the sociology of knowledge*. New York, NY: Doubleday.

Best, J. (2001). *Damned lies and statistics: Untangling numbers from the media, politicians, and activists*. Berkeley, CA: University of California Press.

Best, J. (2004). *More damned lies and statistics: How numbers confuse public issues*. Berkeley, CA: University of California Press.

Boghossian, P. (2006). *Fear of knowledge: Against relativism and constructivism*. Oxford, UK: Clarendon.

Dahl, T. E. (2006). *Status and trends of wetlands in the conterminous United States, 1998 to 2004*. Washington, DC: U.S. Department of Interior, Fish and Wildlife Service.

Hacking, I. (1999). *The social construction of what?* Cambridge, MA: Harvard University Press.

Hilgartner, S., & Bosk, C. L. (1988). The rise and fall of social problems. *American Journal of Sociology*, 94, 53-78.

Oliver, J. E. (2006). *Fat politics: The real story behind America's obesity epidemic*. New York, NY: Oxford University Press.

Paulos, J. A. (1988). *Innumeracy: Mathematical illiteracy and its consequences*. New York, NY: Random House.

Secretaries Norton and Johanns commend gains in U.S. wetlands. (2006). Washington, DC: U.S. Fish and Wildlife Service (news release).

Shell, E. R. (1998, June 28). The Hippocratic wars. *New York Times Magazine*, pp. 34-38.

Study: 1 in 5 students practice self-injury. (2006, June 5). New York, NY: CNN.Com, Time Warner, Inc.

Whitlock, J., Eckenrode, J., & Silverman, D. (2006). Self-injurious behaviors in a college population. *Pediatrics*, 117, 1939-48.

Quantitative Literacy for All:
How Can We Make it Happen

Hugh Burkhardt[*]
University of Nottingham

This paper traces the essential elements of QL—from performance goals, through student learning activities, to their teaching implications and those for teacher education. It takes an engineering research perspective, pointing out that the power of situated learning depends crucially on how well designed and developed the situations are. It sees QL primarily as an end in itself, and a major justification for the large slice of curriculum time that mathematics occupies. It also points out that QL can be a powerful aid to learning mathematical concepts and skills, particularly for those who are not already high achievers.

I approach this important topic from the perspective of an educational engineer. Whereas the 'science research' approach aims for improved *insights* into the system being studied, these are only a starting point for an engineer; 'engineering research', in education as elsewhere, seeks *direct impact* on the system through developing improved tools and/or processes (Burkhardt, 2006). This means that I shall say as much about models and exemplars as about principles and research questions.

---

[*] Hugh Burkhardt is director of the Shell Center for Mathematical Education at the University of Nottingham where has led a series of international projects, notably Balanced Assessment and Mathematics Assessment Resource Service. Burkhardt takes an 'engineering' view of educational research and development: it is about making a complex system work better, with empirical evidence the ultimate guide. His core interest is in the dynamics of curriculum change, seeing assessment as one important tool for change among the many that are needed to help achieve some resemblance between goals of policy and outcomes in practice. As well as assessment, his other interests include real problem solving and mathematical modeling, computer-aided mathematics education, software interface design, and human-computer interaction. He graduated as a theoretical physicist from Oxford University and the University of Birmingham, where he first developed his work on real problem solving. *E-mail*: Hugh.Burkhardt@nottingham.ac.uk.

I shall treat as equivalent the various terms used for QL around the world: *quantitative literacy* or *quantitative reasoning* (US), *functional mathematics* (recent UK), *mathematical literacy* (most other places) and *numeracy* (originally defined in the British Crowther Report (1959) as "the mathematical equivalent of literacy" but now too-often corrupted to mean procedural skill in arithmetic). The distinctions between these terms that people try to make (see e.g. Smith, 2005) are minor compared with the distance of them all from current classroom reality.

In the language of situated learning, this paper looks at two 'activity systems' (Greeno, 1998), the QL classroom and the professional development environment, pre-service and in-service. There is too little space here to discuss the most intractable, the educational systems of which these are part. Though often related to design research (Brown & Campione, 1994), most analyses in terms of situated learning seem to lack the evidential warrants that provide an adequate basis for informing design (Burkhardt & Schoenfeld, 2003). They fail entirely to address the engineering research that is needed to develop products robust enough for effective large-scale use.

What is QL?

PISA (OECD, 2003), representing an international consensus, defines it thus:

> *Mathematical literacy* is an individual's capacity to identify and understand the role that mathematics plays in the world, to make well-founded judgments and to use and engage with mathematics in ways that meet the needs of that individual's life as a constructive, concerned and reflective citizen.

More succinctly, QL is *thinking with mathematics about problems in everyday life*. However, such verbal descriptions on their own are ambiguous—they are easy to re-interpret in terms of one's own experience. I find it clearest to specify performance goals through examples of assessment tasks, with their scoring rubrics, if needed. In the Appendices I offer two tests of mathematical literacy, one appropriate for "all well-educated adults," the second for students around Grade 8. QL is exemplified by the tasks in these tests, perhaps along with some PISA tasks. The notes accompanying each test on the success of those who have tried them confirm that there is work to be done to make QL a reality—no surprise to any of us. Here let us look at just one of these tasks, based on a number of UK cases:

> *Do Sudden Infant Deaths = Murder?* In the general population, about 1 baby in 8,000 dies in an unexplained "crib death." The cause or

causes are at present unknown. Three babies in one family have died. The mother is on trial for murder. A medical expert witness says:

> One crib death is a family tragedy; two is deeply suspicious; three is murder. The odds of even two deaths in one family are 64 million to 1.

Discuss the reasoning behind the expert witness' statement, noting any errors, and write an improved version to present to the jury.

Situated learning and quantitative literacy

How does this task relate to situated learning? The basic idea—that we need to understand learning as an active process in which students have to be engaged constructively—is long familiar, recognized by Dewey and other theorists and restated in the NCTM (1989) Standards as follows: "A person gathers, discovers, or creates knowledge in the course of some activity having a purpose."

At a more detailed level, Engle and Conant (2002) suggest that "productive disciplinary engagement can be fostered by designing learning environments that support:

- problematizing subject matter,
- giving students authority to address such problems,
- holding students accountable to others and to shared disciplinary norms,
- providing students with relevant resources."

Much of the research in the field amounts to rephrasing and refining these ideas, adding illustrations though often with little detail, and distinguishing this from other modes of analysis of learning. Greeno (1998) puts it thus:

> Unlike behaviorist and cognitive research, which focus primarily on individuals, situative research takes larger systems, which we can call *activity systems,* as its primary focus of analysis. An activity system usually has a few people in it, along with whatever resources in the environment that they are interacting with. The main question for the analysis is how such systems function, especially how their components are coordinated.

For this paper the bottom line on situated learning is that meaningful classroom experiences with sense-making produce engaged, empowered, effective learners—not the dominant impression of current mathematics classrooms.

To justify QL as a curriculum component, some mathematicians go further and assert:

For most learners, thinking with mathematics about problems from everyday life offers powerful support for sense making in mathematics.

However true, this is an extraordinarily inward-looking view. For me and, I believe, for most people, the *practical* utility of being able to *think mathematically about practical problems* is the prime motivation for studying mathematics; its inherent beauty and elegance are merely a welcome bonus. I will return to this issue later, after discussing the challenges of making QL a classroom reality.

Tackling real world problems

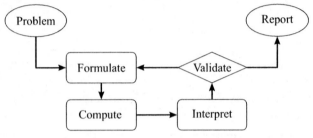

Figure 1. The phases of modeling

The standard diagram in Figure 1, summarizing the top-level processes of QL[1], makes it clear that this involves more complex thinking than the short imitative exercises that dominate mathematics classrooms. However, in the last 40 years, we have learned how to teach the higher-level skills involved (see e.g. Burkhardt with Pollak, 2006). In brief, the following types of student learning activity are necessary:

- *modeling experience* in tackling a range of practical problems using mathematics, without prior teaching on closely similar practical situations—i.e. non-routine problems involving significant transfer distance[2];
- *instruction on strategies for modeling*, a set of heuristics that facilitate the processes of Figure 1;
- *analytical discussion by students of alternative approaches* to a problem, and reflection on the processes involved.

These ingredients are central. How to engineer them into effective curricula at all levels is the still-unfinished story of the last 40 years. However, there is now a well-developed understanding of the key role of modeling and applications in a balanced mathematical education, and some high-quality exemplification of how this can be realized in practice. The recent ICMI Study

14 *Modelling and Applications in Mathematics Education* (Blum, Galbraith, Henn, & Niss, 2007) gives a wide-ranging review of the field.

Details matter: The importance of good engineering

Much of the discussion of QL in the US is, like the text above, about matters of general principle. Probably the most important contribution I can make here is to point out that general principles are not enough—that *the details matter*. The difference between Mozart, Salieri and their many contemporaries of whom we have not heard was not in their general principles—the laws of melody, harmony and counterpoint were common to them all; it lay in their use of those principles in the design and development of their music.

Good engineering recognizes this. Its essential elements are familiar from other fields:

- build on prior work, both research and practice;
- use expert and imaginative designers;
- refine the designs through an iterative process of revisions, based on feedback from trials—ultimately in circumstances of personnel and support like those of the users;
- monitor in the field for rare 'side effects.'

This is a more complicated, and expensive, process than the traditional authorship approach. We compare these approaches in 2.2 and 2.3.

Design heuristics

I say "general principles" because outstanding designers (and composers) work with sets of design strategies and tactics which are often not widely shared or, sometimes, even articulated by the designers. As in any field, many of these are heuristic strategies and tactics, derived directly from experiment—phenomenological and detailed. To take just one powerful example that is relevant to QL (see e.g. Phillips et al., 1988 for evidence): *Moving students into teacher roles leads to higher-level learning.*

Some outstanding teachers can work from general guidance alone. However, many teachers, even if they try, will fail and the whole enterprise may be discredited[3]. Excellence in design and systematic care in development of support will be important in equipping most teachers to make the innovation work in their classrooms. After all, most follow a published text in teaching mathematics they know well. Are they likely to succeed in demanding new areas with *less* support?

Because of its importance, I am going to illustrate this point in some detail, comparing the *traditional approach*, used by innovative teachers and most writers of educational materials, with the more powerful, and more expensive, *research-based* approach of good engineering. Those who produce materials for others to use face two kinds of challenge:

A.   How effectively do the learning activities advance student learning?

B.   How well do the materials communicate the necessary knowledge and skills needed by teacher-users to handle the activities in the classroom?

I will use the problem of *designing a board game* to exemplify the general points. This learning activity, in which students design, construct and evaluate their own games, has often been introduced by innovative teachers in British schools. By way of comparison, we look at a *Numeracy through Problem Solving* module we developed, offering both teaching materials and high-stakes assessment (Shell Centre, 1987–89).

The traditional approach

Most educational materials are written by experienced teachers who seek to show the way they work to fellow professionals. How are new learning activities developed? Let us begin with the board game example. Typically, an innovative teacher asks her students to bring to class their favorite board games. Groups of students play some of these games, thus exploring some existing examples. The teacher then asks each group to design a game of their own, providing an opportunity for creative independent thinking and a product of which they can be proud. This can be a worthwhile activity in which some mathematics may or may not emerge.

However, commercial games are remarkably well-designed and carefully developed; the class has little chance of producing something comparably good. What emerges is usually a minor variant of a commercial game, narrowing the creative horizon. In terms of Question A above, this is a valuable enrichment of any curriculum dominated by imitative exercises but a too-limited experience for the students. The *design load* on the teacher (an important concept) in this approach is large. For the teacher-author, writing up their approach without extensive trialing by others provides no evidence to answer the communication question B.

An engineering research approach

Numeracy through Problem Solving (NTPS) grew from my concern that many students see school mathematics as irrelevant to their present or future lives —except as "something we have to take." Earlier exploratory developments had shown that QL skills can be taught. NTPS was partly inspired by USMES (1969)—and recognition of the unreasonable demands this pioneering project made on teachers.

We started by brainstorming possible topics with a group of exceptional teachers. The 30 topics that seemed promising were looked at through further discussion and some informal trials by the teachers. Some continued to look good; others less so. (*Run a Swap Shop*, in which students bring things they want to barter, was popular but produced classroom chaos. With hindsight we should have seen that $30x29/2$ potential trading pairs was a problem!) We reduced the 30 to 10 and, over 4 years, developed 5 modules.

The design team, led by Malcolm Swan, decided on a 4-stage strategy for the learning sequence. *Design a Board Game* was the first to be developed. It worked out like this:

Stage 1: Students explore the domain by working on and evaluating exemplars provided. For this module we designed five *bad* games. The student's job was to find the (many) faults in each and suggest improvements. For example:

The Great Horse Race Rules

1. Put the horses on their starting positions, 1 to 12.
2. Each player chooses a different horse. If there are only a few players, then each can choose two or three horses. The remaining horses are still in the race but no one 'owns' them.
3. Roll two dice and add the scores.
4. The horse with that number moves one square forward.
5. The first horse to the finish wins.

In *The Great Horse Race* every student can make progress, including many who would normally have great difficulty with the binomial distribution of probabilities. (The games were also designed to bring out mathematical concepts.) The students learned a lot from each game, notably the basics: that a game needs a board, rules for play, and for winning. (They were also delighted that the teaching materials, containing so many mistakes, came from the examination board—an unexpected bonus.)

Note that, because the games had faults, some obvious, others less so, the students' own games were going to be better than these, guaranteeing a feeling of success.

Stage 2: Generate and sift ideas, make a plan. Students in a group share ideas for various new games, choose one, and develop a rough plan for the board and the rules. A great variety of games resulted[4].

Stage 3: Develop and implement the plan in detail. Each group of students produces a detailed design, makes it, and checks the finished version to see it works well, revising if necessary.

Stage 4: Each group evaluates the things that the other groups have produced. The groups exchange games and play them, and write comments. When they are returned, each group re-assesses its own game in the light of another group's comments. The class may or may not vote for favorites.

The design skill, experience and effort exemplified here were matched by an iterative sequence of trials in increasingly representative classrooms. This richness of feedback at all stages is the main difference between these research-based methods and the traditional approach, which relies on the extrapolation of craft-based skills to new situations. Extrapolation is generally unreliable, which is why most fields of product development (engineering, medicine,...) use research-based methods

Assessment in NTPS also follows an unusual model. Embedded assessment tasks test each student's understanding of the ongoing work—important for group projects. For example, the embedded assessment tasks in Stage 1 include finding faults in the following game:

Snakes and Ladders. This is a game for two players. You will need a coin and two counters:

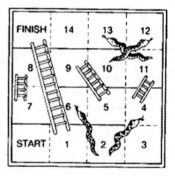

- Take turns to toss the coin. If it is heads, move your counter 2 places forward. If it is tails, move your counter 1 place forward.

- If you reach the foot of a ladder, you must go up it. If you reach the head of a snake, you must go down it.

- The winner is the first player to reach 'FINISH.'

External examinations, some months after the module work, assess their ability to transfer what they had learned to more or less similar problem contexts, within the same domain (here board games) or in structurally related areas. Two general points on assessment design are worth noting:

- The students' common experience of working on the module gives the assessment task designer some control over the transfer distance.

- Rich and open tasks allow responses at a wide range of levels; this is commonly used in other subjects (essays, for example) but underexploited in mathematics.

To summarize: each NTPS module provides learning and teaching materials, with embedded and external assessment; students work in small groups over three weeks per module; each module has real outcomes, with the class evaluating other groups' products. The other four modules are: *Be a Shrewd*

Chooser—how to make better consumer decisions; *Plan a Trip*—for the whole class out of school; *Produce a Game Show*—design and put on a TV quiz; *Be a Paper Engineer*—design pop-up cards and boxes. Students see this type of work as relevant to their current and future lives, especially when everyday contexts *(Shrewd Chooser* or *Trip)* are mixed with others that have an element of fantasy *(Quiz Show, Paper Engineer* and *Board Game)* but develop similar process skills.

Evaluation

The students viewed this as a serious enterprise, working together to develop a product they could be proud of. Most were motivated to take responsibility for the quality of their own and their group's work. Post interviews showed that nearly all students found the work interesting, challenging and enjoyable[5]. When asked to compare this work with "what you normally do in maths," their reaction was surprisingly strong; some groups burst out laughing, explaining that no-one could see their normal mathematics as anything other than a boring imposition. (Their teachers were *not* weak teachers of mathematics.)

Teacher reaction to NTPS was almost as positive. They enjoyed and valued the experience. They were relieved at the end of a module to get back to less taxing teaching, but looked forward to the next module in a few months time. In the outcome, though the modules were developed with students across the ability range, they were used more with low-achieving students—anything that works well with them is welcome, while there is pressure for high-achievers to stick to the standard track.

Parental concerns were addressed with carefully structured parent's meetings. Though they welcomed the "relevance," they had concerns about soft options. These disappeared when they tried problems from the modules and compared their efforts with student work.

Future prospects

After a two decade gap, the British are again taking an active interest in QL. The Bowland Trust and the Government are funding a set of 3–5 lesson "case studies" on a wide range of "real world" topics. We have been asked to develop two: *Reducing road accidents* and *How risky is life?* These are both challenging but we are having fun! The materials are due out in 2008 in electronic and print forms. There have been related developments in Germany and Denmark.

For the US, we are working with some others on a proposal to develop QL units, probably for submission to NSF in due course.

I hope that I have said enough to show how detailed design considerations and careful development can be crucial in the success or failure of general principles. Good engineering of the tools and processes is important in increasing the probability of large-scale success in implementation, for QL as for any profound innovation.

Implications for teaching style

As the discussion of classroom learning confirms, QL cannot be taught with the standard EEE (*explanation–example–exercises*) approach. What extra skills do teachers need? The key elements include:

- *welcoming the world beyond mathematics*, in particular the world of students' lives and their imaginations, in the way that teachers of English and other subjects do;
- *handling discussion in the class in a non-directive but supportive way*, so that students feel responsible for deciding on the correctness of their and others' reasoning and do not expect either answers or confirmation from the teacher;
- *giving students time and confidence* to explore each problem thoroughly, offering help only when the student has tried, and exhausted, various approaches (rather than intervening at the first signs of difficulty);
- *providing strategic and tactical guidance*, rather than showing students who have difficulties how to do the problem, or dividing it into pieces;
- *finding supplementary questions* that build on each student's progress and lead them to go further;
- *helping students to assume responsibility for their own work*, to check their reasoning and their answers and, in discussion with other students, to evaluate the quality of their work.

These are profound changes, implying a change in the "classroom contract" (Brousseau, 1997) of mutual expectations between teacher and students—a change that needs to be made explicit by the teacher[6]. Professionals cannot easily change their well-grooved rituals of practice. The available research shows that this takes time and growing experience based on well-engineered support. The specific foci above will help to provide teachers with a solid start along the path of developing the variety of their mathematical questioning, which is so important in helping students of all abilities reach new levels of achievement.

Among teachers, there is too-often an unfortunate correlation between knowing more mathematics and having an inward-looking view of it[7]. This will make QL an unwelcome challenge for some high school teachers. For elementary and middle school teachers, the challenges of including real world problems are not as great. They have lived in a less specialized world. However, teachers respond to the success of their students, particularly those who find the subject difficult. Their students will flourish in QL.

All this is challenging at first, but teachers who acquire these skills seem to continue to use them; they do not revert to traditional styles. Well-engineered materials can provide enormous support to teachers and students, whether in modeling or in pure mathematical problem solving. Such materials are essential for most teachers in their first few years of such teaching, if they are to achieve success.

The core of the professional development needed is for teachers to gain the same kind of experience of real problem solving as their students will, using much the same materials, and to reflect on the teaching style changes it demands—the focus of the next section.

Who should teach QL?

In the excellent book *Mathematics and Democracy* (Steen, 2002) I was astonished to see the view that QL should not be taught by mathematics teachers as part of the mathematics curriculum, but become a cross-curriculum responsibility. I disagree for the following reasons:

- Teaching QL well is mathematically demanding[8], even for mathematics teachers; those less well-prepared could not cope.
- Utility is the reason why mathematics has such a large slice of curriculum time; in this era of unpredictable future challenges, utility requires QL.
- The cultural importance of mathematics is surely not greater than, say, music; how can this alone justify so much more curriculum time?
- As the experience of statistical education[9] has shown, it is extremely difficult to establish cross-curricular teaching—even harder than introducing a new component into an established subject. If QL is not taught in mathematics, it will not happen.
- QL facilitates the learning of mathematics.

Implications for teacher education

Now, to come at last to the point of this conference, what does this mean for teacher education, both pre-service and in-service? I am no expert in this field, but I am a keen and experienced observer. I know that there are many schools of education around the country and the world for whom the teaching style elements enumerated above (with the probable exception of the first) are already major aims of their programs. For them the main challenge is to enlarge the problem set they build into their courses in the way I have outlined.

QL will prove challenging to many teacher educators in mathematics, who themselves may not use much of their mathematics in their lives outside the classroom[10]. How many of us do 'back of the envelope' estimations to check the assertions of advertisers or politicians? How many would, as a juror or a lawyer, have queried the argument presented by the expert witness in the crib-death problem cited above—elementary though the mathematics is?

Again the way forward is for the teacher educators to gain the same kind of experience of real problem solving as will their students, using much the same materials.

Teachers, like students, benefit from learning constructively—inferring general principles from their own experience of handling specific examples. Our and others' experience favors a *sandwich model*. The essence of this well-established and powerful approach is reflection among teachers, guided by an expert leader and/or well-engineered materials, interleaved with work with students in their classrooms—hence the name. The sequence is:

- *Launch.* Teachers together go through the learning activity in the role of students, then discuss the experience and how they will handle it in the classroom.
- *Teach.* In their own classrooms, the teachers take their students through the activity, collecting samples of student work and, later, making notes on the experience.
- *Reflect.* In the next professional development session, teachers share their experiences and their students' work, reflecting on the learning activity, student responses to it, how they might handle it differently, its wider implication for later lessons in the unit and for other teaching.

This model gives teachers a constructive learning experience, provided it is well-engineered so that the challenges and issues arise in a controlled way, digestible in form and pace, from specific substantial problems. Malcolm Swan (2006) explains the research basis of the sandwich model in the following terms:

"Even in the face of contradictory evidence teachers hold tenaciously onto existing practices. In his literature review, Calderhead (1996) notes how pre-service teachers become more liberal and child-centered during training and then revert to control-oriented belief systems when they enter their full-time career. When well-grooved practices are challenged, then teachers may react both affectively and cognitively. Any attempt to deconstruct someone's beliefs and practices through argument may be perceived as an attack on his or her own identity. Beliefs are more likely to be changed through reflecting on experience than through persuasion. It is only through making pre-existing experiences explicit, challenging them and offering opportunities to examine, elaborate, and integrate new experiences that teachers' behaviors are likely to change.

The situated nature of beliefs may thus mean that it is possible for teachers to adopt a new belief system in a restricted domain, or at least 'suspend disbelief' and act as if they believed differently. They may then subsequently reflect on the experience and accommodate or reject this new belief at least in a tentative way until it may be further tested.

This suggests that we cannot seek to change someone's beliefs so that they will behave differently. Rather, we encourage them to behave differently so that they may have cause to reflect on and modify their beliefs (Fullan, 1991, p.91). Teachers also need the support and resources to experience new ways of working. In the light of this, I suggest the following principles on which I based the development of an in-service program:

- Establish an informal candid culture in which existing beliefs are recognized, made explicit and are worked on in a reflective, non-judgmental atmosphere.

- Illustrate vivid, contrasting practices and discuss the beliefs that underpin these. These may provide 'challenge' or 'conflict.'

- Ask teachers to 'suspend' disbelief and act in new ways, 'as if they believed differently.' Offer mentor and a network of support as they do this.

- Encourage teachers to meet together and reflect on their new experiences and the implications that these offer.

- Ask teachers to reflect on and recognize the growth of new beliefs."

For in-service professional development the sandwich model is often straightforward to organize—participant teachers have their own classes and usually, with discretion and a reasonably supportive principal, can try new things with them.

In view of my inexperience in pre-service teacher preparation programs, my suggestions must be modest but introducing QL here is surely more challenging. The student teacher is a guest in the school, observing and/or substituting for the class teacher in an established program. For schools in which QL is already part of the implemented curriculum, the negotiations should be straightforward. It is made easier for QL than more didactic programs because of the less directive roles needed for teaching QL. Team teaching is an ideal entry mode. For other schools, the best hope may be to 'sell' QL to the principal as an obvious lacuna in mathematics curricula that is now coming onto the agenda. "Wouldn't you like to see what it looks like in the classroom, giving your school a flying start?" The contribution of QL to learning mathematics itself, discussed below, should always be kept in view.

Live in-service teacher education is expensive, but some is essential. It can be made much more effective by using good 'DIY' materials that support ongoing activity among teachers in a school between whatever live sessions may be available and affordable. Past experience shows that providers of live professional development welcome such support for continuing professional development. Is this true for teacher preparation programs?

Assessing teacher effectiveness raises a range of issues beyond the space I have here. I would like to make one obvious point—any methodology should look for changes in a teacher's classroom behavior and relate them to the list enumerated above. Well-designed structured observation before, during and after professional development is rarely part of the development process or of subsequent evaluation[11]; when it is used, it generally leads to radical redesign of the professional development along the lines sketched here.

QL and pure mathematics—not a zero-sum game

Anyone who argues for adding a new element to the curriculum must address the fact that it is seen as already overcrowded. Mathematics texts now have far more pages in them than any teacher can use[12]. One could therefore argue that to add more 'goodies' to the pile changes nothing, except marginally to decrease the already-small chance of anything new being used. More positively, *a significant amount of work on QL can actually reduce the overcrowding* by reducing the large amount of time (up to 35%) spent *re-teaching* concepts and skills (an ineffective approach to remedying misconceptions).

Modeling real world situations supports the learning of mathematical concepts and skills in several ways:

    (a) It provides multiple *concrete embodiments* of mathematical concepts;

    (b) It builds fluent *translation skills* between different representations;

    (c) It involves *extended chains of reasoning*; for which

(d) It requires *procedural accuracy*, so encourages *checking* (not moving on regardless).

Indeed, many active proponents of modeling are mainly motivated by its power in teaching mathematics better. The Freudenthal Institute team, for example, say explicitly that the prime goal of their *Realistic Mathematics Education (RME)* approach is deeper understanding of mathematics itself. *Mathematics in Context* materials show this focus. The contributions of modeling to other mathematical competencies is surveyed in ICMI Study 14 (Blum, Galbraith, Henn, & Niss, 2007) in Section 3.4 which I (somewhat ironically, given my priorities) was asked to co-edit.

To illustrate (a), let us return to *The Great Horse Race* discussed earlier and the discussion by Swan et al (*ibid.* Section 3.4.1) of the concept formation it supports.

> All students quickly recognize that Horse 1 is not a good bet! A few have the misconception that, because there are two dice, higher numbered horses will move more rapidly. Even they, through playing the game, soon realize that horses in the middle will move faster "because there are more ways of making 7 than 11 or 12." Most will enumerate these "1+6, 2+5, 3+4..."; some initially miss that 4+3 is different from 3+4 until the teacher suggests two different colored dice. More advanced students consider the effect of the length of the track on the likely outcome. This game thus proves an effective (and quick) stimulus to concept formation. Furthermore if every student colors the squares traversed by each horse, they obtain a frequency distribution. When these are displayed around the classroom, students have an immediate visual of the variability of sample data. If the teacher enters these data in a spreadsheet, the frequency distribution of the totals will provide a better fit to the theoretical probabilities than will those of individual students.

The detailed design of this activity, guided by the student book, is crucial to its power and range. Its robustness in classroom use, not to mention some design ideas, comes from revisions, each guided by the feedback from successive rounds of closely observed trials. *In situated learning the quality of the situation is crucial.*

On translation skills, (b) above, when students work on modeling tasks, they express their thoughts in a variety of representations: words, diagrams, tables, spreadsheets, graphs, algebraic expressions. Indeed, many real world problems begin with information provided in a variety of representations. Since any representational medium will highlight some aspects of the structure, while obscuring others, students who engage in modeling activities develop *translation skills*—the ability to move information between different representations.

Items (c) and (d) above are self-evident. On (d), note how the pay-off from checking changes from short items to longer chains of reasoning which, if they are not correct throughout, leave you completely at sea.

Shorter modeling activities, too, have a part to play in both QL and the developing of robust mathematical skills. The interpretation of graphical information, reflecting (b), is one example (see Swan *et al.*, 1986)

Finally, it is important to absorb the distinction, summarized in Figure 2, between:

- *standard applications* of a mathematical topic, and
- *active modeling* of a *non-routine* practical situation, to which several mathematical tools usually contribute.

Each is a necessary part of QL but they have different roles.

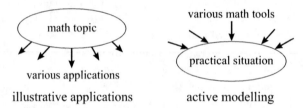

Figure 2. Standard illustrative applications v non-routine active modelling

Standard illustrative applications provide links between the real world problems and your mathematics toolkit. They can often be adapted to help with new problems—indeed all problem solving involves recognizing familiar structural features in a problem situation. However, tackling new problems effectively depends on experience with the processes of active modeling, supported by some teaching of the strategies and tactics that help in using one's mathematical toolkit to be more quantitatively literate.

A few key points

The following points may be worth restating:

- For QL, as with all situated learning, the quality of the situation is central to success.
- Most teachers will need at least as much support, in both materials and live teacher education, as they expect in familiar areas of mathematics teaching.

- High quality in both materials and processes depends on combining research awareness, imaginative design, and careful development of products and processes— an engineering research approach.

- Teacher education for this less familiar mathematical competency should be through constructive learning, involving teachers and teacher educators in the mathematical activities, linked to reflection on their implications for both the subject and its teaching.

- QL will help students learn more pure mathematics more effectively, building deeper understanding, richer connections and greater accuracy. This is particularly true for weaker students, narrowing "the gap."[13]

Acknowledgements. I thank many colleagues, particularly Malcolm Swan, Daniel Pead, Alan Bell and Rita Crust.

References

Blum, W., Galbraith, P., Henn, W., & Niss, M. (Eds.). (2007). *Modelling and applications in mathematics education.* Heidelberg, Germany: Springer Academics (former Kluwer Academics).

Brousseau, G. (1997). *Theory of didactical situations in mathematics* (Didactique des mathématiques), 1970–1990. Ed. and trans. by Balacheff, N. Dordrecht, Netherlands: Kluwer.

Brown, A. L. & Campione, J. C. (1994). Guided discovery in a community of learners. In K. McGilly (Ed.), *Classroom lessons: Integrating cognitive theory and classroom practice* (pp. 229–270). Cambridge, MA: MIT Press.

Burkhardt, H. (2006). From design research to large-scale impact: Engineering research in education. In J. Van den Akker, K. Gravemeijer, S. McKenney, & N. Nieveen (Eds.), *Educational design research* (pp. 121–150). London, UK: Routledge.

Burkhardt, H. with contributions from Pollak, H. O. (2006). Modelling in mathematics classrooms: reflections on past developments and the future. *Zentralblatt für Didaktik der Mathematik*, 39 (2), 178–195.

Burkhardt, H., & Schoenfeld, A.H. (2003). Improving educational research: toward a more useful, more influential and better funded enterprise. *Educational Researcher*, 32, 3-14.

Calderhead, J. (1996). Teacher beliefs and knowledge. In D. Berliner & R. Calfe (Eds.) *Handbook of educational psychology* (pp. 709–725). New York, NY: Simon and Schuster Macmillan.

Crowther Report 15-18. (1959). *A report of the central advisory council for education.* London, UK: HMSO.

Engle, R.A. & Conant, F.R. (2002). Guiding principles for fostering productive disciplinary engagement. *Cognition and Instruction*, 20(4), 399–483.

Fullan, M. G. (1991). *The new meaning of educational change.* London, UK: Cassell.

Greeno, J.R. (2002). *Students with competence, authority and accountability.* New York, NY: The College Board.

NCTM. (1989). *Curriculum and evaluation standards.* Reston, VA: National Council of Teachers of Mathematics

OECD. (2003). The PISA 2003 Assessment framework: Mathematics, reading, science and problem solving knowledge and skills. Paris, FR: OECD. www.pisa.oecd.org/dataoecd/38/51/33707192.pdf

Phillips, R.J., Burkhardt, H., Fraser, R., Coupland, J., Pimm, D., & Ridgway, J. (1988). Learning activities & classroom roles with and without the microcomputer. *J. Math. Behavior*, 6, 305–338.

Shell Centre (1984). Swan, M., Pitt, J., Fraser, R. E., & Burkhardt, H., with the Shell Centre team, *Problems with patterns and numbers.* Manchester, UK: Joint Matriculation Board; reprinted 2000, Nottingham, UK: Shell Centre Publications.

Shell Centre: Swan, M., Binns, B., Gillespie, J., and Burkhardt, H. (1987-89). *Numeracy through problem solving.* Harlow, UK: Longman; reissued 2000, Nottingham, UK: Shell Centre Publications.

Smith Report. (2004). *Making mathematics count.* London, UK: Department For Education and Skills, HMSO. Retrieved Nov. 13, 2005, www.mathsinquiry.org.uk/report /index.html.

Steen, L. A. (Ed). (2002). *Mathematics and democracy: The case for quantitative literacy,* Princeton, NJ: National Council on Education and the Disciplines.

Swan, M. with the Shell Centre team: (1986). *The language of functions and graphs,* Manchester, UK: Joint Matriculation Board; reprinted 2000, Nottingham, UK: Shell Centre Publications.

Swan M. (2006). *Collaborative learning in mathematics* (pp. 170 ff). London, UK: National Research and Development Centre and National Institute of Adult Continuing Education.

USMES. (1969). *Unified sciences and mathematics for elementary schools*: books.nap.edu/openbook/0309052939/html/129.html

Appendix A: Functional Mathematics for Educated Adults

A few thought-provoking tasks that any well-educated adult could, and should, be able to do without having been taught the specific problem, selected from the Mathematics Assessment Resource Service (MARS), Shell Centre for Mathematical Education, University of Nottingham. Commentary on the tasks and responses to them appears at the end of the appendix.

Sudden Infant Deaths = Murder?

In the general population, about 1 baby in 8,000 dies in an unexplained "crib death". The cause or causes are at present unknown. Three babies in one family have died. The mother is on trial. An expert witness says:

One crib death is a family tragedy; two is deeply suspicious; three is murder. The odds of even two deaths in one family are 64 million to 1.

Discuss the reasoning behind the expert witness' statement, noting any errors, and write an improved version to present to the jury.

Conference Budget

Your job is to plan a conference budget, using a computer spreadsheet. You have already made a start:

  (i) Complete the entries for Wednesday in column D.

  (ii) Calculate appropriate totals in column E.

(The spreadsheet was on a computer.)

A	B	C	D	E
	College charges	Number	@ £ each	£
Monday	Buffet Supper	30	17.00	0
	Single En-suite Accommodation	30	40.00	0
Tuesday	Breakfast	30	8.00	0
	Morning Coffee	30	1.90	0
	Luncheon	30	15.00	0
	Afternoon tea	30	1.90	0
	Dinner served	30	50.00	0
	Single En-suite Accommodation	30	40.00	0
	Plenary Room	30	15.77	0
	Breakout rooms	2	85.10	0
Wednesday	Breakfast	30		0
	Morning Coffee	30		0
	Luncheon	30		0
	Afternoon tea	30		0
	No Dinner	30		0
	Single En-suite Accommodation	30		0
	Plenary Room	30		0
	Breakout rooms	2		0
Thursday	Breakfast	30	8.00	0
	Morning Coffee	30	1.90	0
	Luncheon	30	15.00	0
	Afternoon tea	30	1.90	0
	Dinner	30	17.00	0
	Single En-suite Accommodation	30	40.00	0
	Plenary Room	30	15.77	0
	Breakout rooms	2	85.10	0
Friday	Breakfast	30	8.00	0
			Total charges	0
			VAT	0
			Total	0

Elementary School Teachers

In a country with 300 million people, about how many elementary school teachers will be needed? Try to estimate a sensible answer using your own everyday knowledge about the world. Write an explanation of your answer, stating any assumptions you make.

Bike or Bus

Terry is soon to go to secondary school. There is no school bus. The bus trip costs $1 and Terry's parents are considering the alternative of buying him a bicycle.

Help Terry's parents decide what to do by carefully working out the relative merits of the two alternatives.

Right Turns

The truck is stopped at traffic lights, planning to turn right. The cycle is alongside.

If the cyclist waits for the truck to turn before moving, what will happen? Explain why this will happen with a diagram.

What would be your advice: to the truck driver? to the cyclist? Give reasons in each case.

Scheduling Traffic Lights

A new set of traffic lights has been installed at an intersection formed by the crossing of two roads. Right turns are *not* permitted at this intersection.

For how long should each road be shown the green light? Explain your reasoning clearly.

Being Realistic About Risk

"My sixty-year-old mother, who lives in New York, gets frightened by newspapers. One day she is afraid of being a victim of crime, the next she is frightened of being killed in a road accident, then it's terrorists, and so on."

> (i) Use a website with national statistics to estimate the chances of my mother being a victim of the above events, and others you think she might worry about.
>
> (ii) Write down some reassurance you would give her—and compare the likelihood of these events with the probability that women of her age will die during the coming year.

Commentary on the tasks, and responses to them:

Sudden Infant Deaths = Murder? What we expect here is not a full statistical analysis, which would need more information, but a recognition that the reasoning presented is deeply flawed. There are two elementary mistakes in the statement, and one that is a bit more subtle. It would be correct to say:

1. The chance of these deaths being entirely *unconnected* chance events is very small indeed—if there has been one death, the chance of two more unconnected deaths is about 64 million to one.

2. What can the connection be? It may be that the mother killed the children; on the other hand, particularly since we do not understand the cause(s) of crib death, there may be other explanations. For many conditions (cancer and heart disease, for example) genetic and environmental factors are known to affect the probability substantially.

Any lawyer or judge with functional mathematics should have seen problems with the witness statement. It is not lack of basic skills that was their failing (They could surely have worked out the chance of a double six on rolling two dice as 1/36) but an understanding of the necessary assumptions.

Conference Budget. This is a task we give (on a working spreadsheet) to candidates for the post of Secretary/Administrator in the team. Most are graduates. All "know Excel". None complete the task. Most see that Wednesday's values in Column D are probably the same as Tuesday's and Thursday's. Few enter the appropriate, or indeed any, formulas in Column E. (Formulating relationships is a basic piece of algebra that is neglected in schools—and mathematics tests.) Some even work out the row totals on a calculator, entering the *values*!

Elementary School Teachers. This kind of back-of-the-envelope calculation is an important life skill. Here it requires choosing appropriate facts (6 years in elementary school out of a life of 60-80 years, one teacher for 20-30 kids), and formulating appropriate proportional relationships giving $(300*6)/(70*25)$ ~ 1 million primary teachers (to an accuracy appropriate to that of the data). This kind of linkage with the real world, common in the English language arts curriculum, is rare in school mathematics (and absent in tests).

Bike or Bus and Scheduling Traffic Lights. See *Ice Cream Van* in Appendix B.

Right Turns. Functional mathematics often involves space and shape, too.

Being Realistic About Risk. Education, and functional mathematics in particular, can help narrow the gap between perceived and real risk. Given the power of anecdote over evidence, exploited daily by the media, this is a major challenge; meeting it could make a huge contribution to people's quality of life, and that of their children. Few people have any sense of the magnitude of specific risks, or any idea of the unavoidable 'base risk' for someone of their age. (Note that only order-of-magnitude estimates, not accurate numbers, are relevant here.)

Explicitly teaching students to use their mathematics on real problems is now proven, with typical teachers; it is essential to functionality. These exemplars also show how deterministic and statistical reasoning intermesh in functional mathematics.

Appendix B
Functional Mathematics for Grade 8 or 9

A few thought-provoking tasks that any well-educated student should be able to do by age 15 without having been taught the specific problem, selected from the Mathematics Assessment Resource Service (MARS), Shell Centre for Mathematical Education, University of Nottingham. Commentary on the tasks and responses to them appears at the end of the appendix.

Freeway Journey

Referring to the figure below:

- Do they have to stop for gas? Explain your reasoning.
- Suppose they decide to stop for 10 minutes. At what time will they reach Los Angeles?

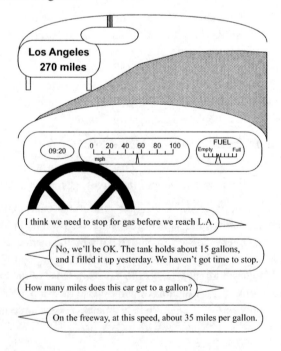

At the Airport

Den's Currency Exchange		
Currency	We Buy	We Sell
$ US Dollar	£ 0.533	£ 0.590
€ Euro	£ 0.660	£ 0.730
No commission!		

How many Euros (€) would you get for £500?

How many Pounds (£) can you get for $700?

How much would you have to pay, in Pounds and Pence, to get exactly €550?

Paper Clips

This paper clip is just over 4 cm long. How many paper clips like this may be made from a straight piece of wire 10 meters long?

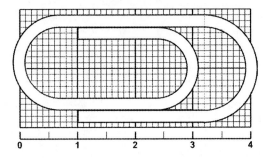

Ice Cream Van

You are considering driving an ice cream van during the Summer break. Your friend, who "knows everything", says that "It's easy money". You make a few enquiries and find that the van costs $600 per week to hire. Typical selling data is that one can sell an average of 30 ice creams per hour, each costing 50c to make and each selling for $1.50.

How hard will you have to work in order to make this "easy money"? Explain your reasoning clearly.

Cold Calling

The following is part of a genuine letter of complaint to a bank.

I would like to complain about the behavior of XYZ Bank and the advice given during a recent unsolicited telephone call. Having been told I was "pre-approved" for a $5,000 loan, the operator asked me for my financial details. I told her that I currently had two credit cards, one with a balance of $3000 and one with $1000. She said that they could consolidate these debts into a single payment which would be cheaper. I pressed her on the APR which she explained was 16.4%, which caused me to decline the loan because my two credit cards are currently at 7% and 9.9% APR respectively. The operator then informed me that their loan would work out cheaper, because 7% and 9.9% works out at 16.9%, nearly 0.5% higher than the bank loan.

(i)   Explain what is wrong with the operator's reasoning.

(ii) How much more expensive is the bank's consolidated loan?

Commentary on the tasks, and responses to them

Motorway Journey. From an actual test. Most examples of functional mathematics have been eliminated in the fragmentation of tasks to assess separate micro-skills.

At the Airport. It is interesting to compare this with a question from a current UK school test (on the right). Note how the simplification of the presentation leaves a major gap from real functionality. This unreality, characteristic of secondary school mathematics, confirms many students' view that the subject has no relevance to their lives.

The table shows the exchange rates between different currencies:

£1 (Pound)	is worth	€ 1.45 (Euros)
$1 (Dollar)	is worth	€ 0.81 (Euros)

(a) Jane changes £400 into euros. How many euros does she receive?

(b) Sonia changes £672 euros into dollars. How many dollars does she receive?

Ice Cream Van. This task was used in a research study of the performance of 120 very able 17-year-old students. Many solved the tasks, using arithmetic and, sometimes graphs. *None used algebra*, the natural language for formulating such problems. Their algebra was non-functional, despite 5+ years of high success in the standard imitative inward-looking algebra curriculum.

Paper Clips. This task exemplifies a step towards functionality; a school mathematics version is shown on the right.

Cold Calling. A common misconception, and con, to unravel. Explicitly teaching students to use

A semi-circle has a diameter of 12 cm. Calculate the perimeter.

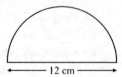

their mathematics on real problems is now proven, with typical teachers; it is essential to functionality. These exemplars also show how deterministic and statistical reasoning intermesh in functional mathematics.

Endnotes

[1] Pure mathematical problem solving has a similar structure, though there are important differences.

[2] *Transfer distance* is a measure of how different two problems are, and so of how non-routine a task is, how far it differs from tasks with which the student is familiar. An important concept, no-one has seriously tackled the interesting challenge of inventing a practical way to quantify it, perhaps partly because it depends on the student's whole prior experience.

[3] I see the history of "problem solving" in US schools in the 1980s as an instance of this. After adoption by NCTM as a theme, much general advice was made available but little or no fully developed teaching material. Not much happened. At the Shell Centre we adopted a different approach, working with an examination board to develop coordinated *pressure* (new high-stakes exam tasks) and *support* (new teaching materials). These are published in (Shell Centre, 1984).

[4] In a few schools, the teachers decided to make this a joint project with the Art or Design departments, with excellent results. We encouraged this, but making this a requirement would have killed the project—and its effect on student attitudes to mathematics.

[5] The exceptions were a small proportion of normally high-achieving students who found being faced with a new 'game' of a different kind somewhat threatening.

[6] When we began to develop support for problem solving in pure mathematics (Shell Centre 1984), the first exploratory set of examples we gave to students was headed "THIS IS NOT A MATHS EXAM." It was, of course, but not what they expected of one.

[7] The evaluation of the USMES project (1969) found that mathematics teachers were the worst USMES teachers; the best were "drop-out Art teachers!" A case can be made for "style specialization" —teaching investigation is as far from traditional EEE mathematics teaching as teaching some other subjects. Let those math teachers who can do it, concentrate on it.

[8] "....the sophisticated use of elementary mathematics," in Lynn Steen's immortal phrase, is not something to expect from those with weak mathematics.

[9] Statistics educators have always seen QL as central and, mainly for this reason, sought to separate themselves from mathematics education; however, this separation is unhelpful. Many problems should be tackled deterministically, at least initially; sometimes the analysis must take random variation into account. (Statistics has no monopoly on data.)

[10] The "test for well-educated adults" in Appendix A is a useful self-evaluation tool.

[11] Indeed there are those who would regard classroom observation as unpardonably intrusive, regarding professional development as a civilized exchange between fellow professionals in which the sole criterion of success is whether the teacher found the experience valuable.

[12] This is primarily because they are designed, not for teachers, but for the state adoption processes of Texas and California. To be considered, let alone adopted, text packages have to check every box on a list that seems to be the union of the wishes of the members of the adoption committee. From this wish-list, teachers select what they want to use—often just what they know well.

[13] ... but not guaranteeing the early fluency in *abstract* algebra that seems to be a prime current goal in the U.S.

The Licensure of Teachers for Quantitative Literacy: Who Should Be Entitled to Teach QL?

Frank B. Murray
University of Delaware

The United Kingdom's Department for Education and Skills defines *numeracy*, otherwise know as *quantitative literacy* in the United States, somewhat broadly and imprecisely as follows:

> Numeracy is a proficiency which is developed mainly in mathematics but also in other subjects. It is more than an ability to do basic arithmetic. It involves developing confidence and competence with numbers and measures. It requires understanding of the number system, a repertoire of mathematical techniques, and an inclination and ability to solve quantitative or spatial problems in a range of contexts. Numeracy also demands understanding of the ways in which data are gathered by counting and measuring, and presented in graphs, diagrams, charts and tables.

There is no inherent reason that the symbol systems associated with ordinary literacy and language would be intrinsically different from the system entailed in quantitative literacy as the mind seems to be equivalently disposed to support both language and numeracy. Wynn (1992), for example, argues that humans are innately endowed with arithmetical abilities, and she and others

---

Frank B. Murray is H. Rodney Sharp Professor in the School of Education and Department of Psychology at the University of Delaware. He served as dean of the College of Education between 1979 and 1995. Currently, he is President of the Teacher Accreditation Council (TEAC) in Washington, DC. His Ph.D. is from Johns Hopkins University and for his contributions to the fields of child development and teacher education, he was awarded an honorary doctorate from Heriot-Watt University in Edinburgh, Scotland in 1994. E-mail: fmurray@udel.edu.

163

have found evidence of numeracy in infants as young as 3–5 months (equivalence of sets, ordinal discrimination, addition/subtraction, cross-modal numeric sensitivity). Basic numeracy (determining the number of objects without counting, ordinality, counting, number conservation, simple arithmetic) seems governed by innate developmental mechanisms, because numeracy emerges spontaneously in all cultures and in all typical environments. It seems also to be the case (Ferrari & Sternberg, 1998) that these basic actions are performed by rote initially, and only later, reinforced by the culture, do they acquire a conceptual representation along with some learned strategies (e.g., finger counting, min or count-on), procedural knowledge (it is illegal to divide by zero), translation of verbal statements into numerical propositions (dozen refers to 12), and certain beliefs (mathematics requires innate ability, is for men, or that there is only one right answer in mathematics).

Crosby (1997) makes a case that historically the well-understood and transforming effects of language on cognition are also found for quantification. His thesis is that in the late thirteenth century a new way of thinking emerged that quantified time (the first mechanical clocks), space (drawing in perspective), finances (double-entry bookkeeping) and visualized reality as aggregates of uniform quantified units—leagues, miles, pounds, hours, minutes, and musical notes—that expanded numbers from their nominal and ordinal properties, available beforehand in ordinary language, to the powerful additional properties of equal intervals and ratios, which are available to the "counting person" only when there is true quantification.

The concept, *quantitative literacy*, seeks an analog to ordinary literacy, crudely measured by whether a person can read and write, to something that transcends proficiency in four function arithmetic to a sensitivity to the quantitative dimensions of all experience, to an amalgam of skills, knowledge, dispositions that can be applied to the quantitative dimensions of experience, and to an interpretation of a new reality of the sort portrayed by Crosby's thesis, but beyond the areas he described to all areas of experience. The question is what kind of teacher education program, supported by what kind of licensing requirements, license tests, national board certificates, etc. would support increased levels of quantitative literacy in the schools. To what course of study should the prospective teacher be exposed and how can that be captured in the state's licensing protocols.

Take the following example[1] of quantitative literacy as it demonstrates the "developing confidence and competence with numbers and measures. It requires understanding of the number system, a repertoire of mathematical techniques, and an inclination and ability to solve quantitative or spatial problems in a range of contexts." It is a lesson given by a teacher whose pupils had been taught previously the standard definitional lesson on odd and even numbers and were now exploring patterns in them, such as *an even number plus an even number is always an even number*. One of the pupils, Sean, offered the conjecture that some numbers are both odd and even.

Of course there are no numbers that are both odd and even, and the teacher now has a dilemma that also goes to the heart of the question of how the teacher education program would have prepared a teacher for this dilemma, what knowledge would be needed, and where could it have been acquired in traditional higher education? The larger question of this paper is how the teaching licensing and program accreditation regulations could capture (or frustrate) what was needed to encourage the pursuit of quantitative literacy at this juncture in the lesson.

Should time be taken from the next topic in the state's prescribed curriculum to review this topic, a topic that would have only one or two items on the state's standardized test? Should the teacher tell Sean he is mistaken and correct him by simply restating clearly the odd-even numbers definition for him and be done with it? Or, should Sean's conjecture be pursued to some mathematical conclusion.

What kind of teacher education program would support the teacher's pursuit of Sean's assertion, nonsensical as it might seem? Quantitative literacy in fact is partly defined by a confidence to pursue the issue in this situation even though the teacher would surely never have come across such an idea in any teacher education program of study. It is equally certain, by the way, that that these numbers of Sean's conjecture would never be on any standardized test of number understanding. This fact only complicates the links between quantitative literacy, teacher education, and the licensing and accreditation regulations.

When Sean was asked, by the teacher how he thought some numbers were both odd and even, he replied with the novel observation that six was such an odd-even number because two went into it an odd number of times while eight was not such a number because two went into it an even number of times.

The teacher went to the heart of quantitative literacy instruction[2] by asking the class to consider whether Sean's conjecture had any merit. The class worked out the pattern that every other even number was one of these even-odd Sean numbers—six was, eight was not, ten was, twelve was not, but fourteen was and so forth. Others explored whether adding Sean numbers together gave another Sean number or gave non-Sean even numbers. Others noted that adding Sean numbers and non-Sean even numbers always yielded a Sean number. The same relationships held for subtraction while other outcomes held for the multiplication of odd, Sean and non-Sean even numbers.

After further exploration of the properties and patterns of Sean numbers, the class was asked whether these odd-even even numbers should be added to the list of numbers the class had studied (real, rational, integer, natural, complex, etc,) . How should they even decide whether Sean numbers should be added to the mathematics curriculum? Should they vote on it, or is democracy a poor mathematical procedure? And if they voted on it, should the decision be based on a simple majority, super majority, unanimity, should it be accompanied by confidence ratings, and so on? Each of these options demands some level of quantitative literacy.

This particular example showcases an unscripted and unplanned teaching event, what some might call a *teachable moment,* but it is more than that as it also represents the core of quantitative literacy—a confidence to tackle an uncharted quantitative matter, serviceable knowledge of mathematical procedure and knowledge, logical thought and problem-solving, an extension of the quantitative into the political and social, and so forth.

One of the problems with the assessment of quantitative literacy in these contexts is that standardized tests, favored by policy-makers who would hold teacher's accountable for their teaching, are quite distant from what goes on the class and are restricted to what was hoped went on in the class and what lends itself to easy measurement. A second problem is that the public really learns more about what did not go on in the school than what did, because the lower the test scores, the less we actually know about what went on in the classroom. The test would not reveal whether the teacher taught what was on the test poorly, or whether the teacher taught something else, like Sean's conjecture very well. A third problem is that the published standards, like the standards for numeracy, for the information that should be covered by the tests are usually so vague and abstract that almost nothing is ruled in or out of the curriculum (see Raths, 1999; Ohanian, 1999 & 2000).

There are at least two competing views in the nation, today and historically, about what teachers need to know and how they should be prepared. More about each is discussed later, but both views hold that teachers, regardless of what else they know, must know the subject matters they hope to teach their pupils. The academic major, the usual remedy, can be shown, however, to be an inadequate preparation in the subject matter the prospective teacher will teach. Mathematics majors, for example, are no better than non-math majors in creating real world examples of the division of one fraction by another[3]. By and large, the academic major does not induce in students the kind of penetrating understanding necessary to pursue Sean's conjecture or other novel notions in quantitative literacy. Efforts to reform the academic major have not abandoned the concept of the academic major itself, but rather have tried to make the academic major more effective, especially for teachers, who seek to acquire a special kind of integrative subject-matter knowledge that would undergird complex areas like quantitative literacy. Proposed solutions have centered on new majors, interdisciplinary majors, and new types of courses within existing majors.

The case of the appropriate course of study for the elementary school, or social studies, or quantitative literacy teacher across the grades is particularly instructive because it illustrates the knotty problems that arise when teachers must acquire a wider range of knowledge than the typical academic major covers. In the case of the elementary school teacher it is difficult to see how the prospective elementary teachers would become well-grounded in mathematics, literature, writing, history, geography, the natural and social sciences, the fine arts, language—all subjects that are taught in grade school classroom. At the secondary level the matter is only a little less complicated for social studies or general science, which are informed by several distinct university subjects or majors, each of which is a full university course of study in its own right. The most promising preparation for quantitative literacy, an even wider domain than social studies or general science, is likely to be informed by proposals to solve the problem of the appropriate academic major for the elementary teacher. Six options are promising (see Murray, 1991 for an expanded account).

1. Interdisciplinary major. This option is a collection of reworked minors in the areas of the school curriculum: mathematics, foreign language, history and social science, English, natural science, and fine arts. Apart from the fact that each minor would be responsive to the unique requirements of the elementary school teacher, the interdisciplinary minor option is fairly conservative and administratively feasible. It is an honest approach insofar as each major area of the elementary school curriculum is addressed. A similar approach can be imagined for the teacher who is sensitive to quantitative literacy as the opportunities for this extension occur in each minor.

2. Philosophy of subject matter. In this approach the philosophy of each subject matter (e.g., philosophy of science, mathematics, etc.) is taken up, and essential and fundamental aspects of the structure of subject matter are covered. Teachers learn, for example, that there are no facts apart from theories or that "true" theories are not those that were proved, but only those that have failed to be disproved. Similarly, social studies education learn to view the history curriculum not so much as a chronology, or as the true view of the past, but as one of several possible stories of the past that could be constructed to make sense of the same historical events. Teachers learn of the similarities in the grammar and syntax of mathematics and language, and so on.

This approach is related to the so-called *structure of the disciplines* approach to curriculum reform that followed the Sputnik educational crisis some forty years ago. The underlying coherent principles or structures that hold academic disciplines together are the subject of the courses themselves in this approach. The separate natural sciences, for example, can be organized by the principle of evolution (evolution of species, matter, solar systems, societies and cultures, sub-atomic particles, chemical reactions, etc.). Or they can be organized by the principle of orders of magnitude (e.g., the powers of 10 device of relating sub-atomic structure, biochemistry, and celestial systems as well as the design constraints of other physical and animate structures that stem from their size alone). Whatever it is that makes a certain kind of study, *numeracy,* and not some other kind of study, is the subject of this approach to improving the teacher's capacity for teaching quantitative literacy.

3. Text approach or "great books" major. This approach entails an unusual course of study that contains a close reading of seminal texts, or founding texts, in each area (the "great books") coupled with an examination of school textbooks for the assumptions they make about the discipline in question. The logic of this proposal, like the philosophy of the disciplines approach, is that the core structure of the discipline is addressed directly, and the "forest for the trees" problem that plagues most university study is minimized. The logic has a pedagogical dimension as well, because the student is introduced to the discipline in the way that approximates how world was first introduced to it.

The six topics (pattern, dimension, uncertainty, shape, and change) taken up by Steen (1990) are reasonable candidates for the numeracy "great books" topics along with the traditional mathematics notions, like number.

4. Genetic epistemology. This option entails the study of the developmental psychological literature from the perspective of the development of the concepts that make up the curriculum. In this approach the prospective teacher learns the relevant developmental constraints upon the pupil's acquisition of the curriculum and lays out, as an unavoidable part of the discussion, the nature of the subject itself. The story of how the young child develops the notion of number, for example, is valuable in its own right, but also reveals salient portions of number theory, the arithmetical algorithms, and other aspects of mathematics. Similarly, the account of the child's moral development reveals the principal issues in moral philosophy and political theory. The scientific account of how children form groups and gangs, establish rules for games, assign blame and praise, identify enemies, punish transgressions, acquiesce and conform to other's wishes and requirements, advance their position, and so forth are instructive for the counterparts of these and other issues in history and political and social science. Thus, the prospective teacher acquires important knowledge about both the student's mind and the content of the discipline they hope to teach.

5. The cognitive psychology major. In this option the prospective teacher would study a reformed major in cognitive psychology in which the working of the mind in various domains becomes the specialization. The subject matter content would be picked up through the consideration of how the mind operates mathematically, aesthetically, historically and so forth. Like the philosophy of the disciplines or text approaches, this approach would provide a structure for the reformed minors in each subject area. Each area would be approached from the perspective of how we think about and know the content in question. The approach fits well with the current recognition in cognitive psychology that thinking is domain specific.

While our notions of number, transitivity, class inclusion, necessity, probability, and so forth are each objects of study in cognitive psychology, the study of the concept of *time* is illustrative. A well-developed notion of *time,* which supports, for example, an understanding of daylight savings time takes about eighteen years to acquire.[4] The properties of the numbers that designate time, like the numbers assigned to years, are not appreciated by elementary school children who can be shown not to grasp order of these numbers or that the intervals between them are equal. A young child will argue that the taller of two trees planted at the same moment is older, that the corroded coin of two minted in the same year is older, and so on. Older children will argue that the clock actually runs slower and faster at certain times of the day and year. The point is that immediate time, let alone historical time, is a fragile concept for the child and the young adolescent. It cannot be merely assumed by the teacher that the order and intervals between dates, for example, have anything like the meaning they may have for the teacher.

6. The pedagogical content knowledge minor. This approach addresses the fact that teachers inevitably transform what they know into a teachable subject. They give the subject a new structure and meaning, one that is appropriate to their students' level of understanding. These structures can be studied and codified. Since this reformulation of the discipline is inevitable in teaching, one might as well address it directly and, as in the other approaches, use it as a way to structure and teach the academic disciplines. In teaching *Huckleberry Finn,* for example, the teacher inevitably interprets the book as a story of race relations, or generation gaps, or an historical period, or latent homosexuality on the frontier, or whatever. The academic major would explicitly address these pedagogical alternatives. As another example, many science teachers attempt to clarify the nature of electric current by comparing it to the behavior of water currents in various sized pipes, and so forth. Is this a good way to think about electricity, particularly alternating current? How would one know? The answer to the question is not to be found in physics or in education, but in a qualitatively different kind of knowledge that will come from conversations between disciplinarians and pedagogues and one that builds upon genetic epistemology and cognitive science.

In the earlier example of the division of fractions (1¾ by the fraction ½), once the division by 2 error is cleaned up, are the following representations of the mathematics pedagogically equivalent and equally commendable—How many half slices are there in 1¾ pizza pies? How many 50 cent tickets can be bought for $1.75? How many half pint cans of oil are needed to exactly fill of 1 ¾ pint engine? How many half yard ruffles are needed to cover the bottom of a dress of 1¾ yard's circumference? How could the equivalence and merit be determined?

This knowledge—the knowledge of what is a telling example, a good analogy, a provocative question, or a compelling theme—is a proper object of study and could yield a deep and generative understanding of the disciplines of quantitative literacy. To have multiple ways of representing a subject matter, to have more than one example or metaphor, to have more than one mode of explanation requires a high order and demanding form of subject matter understanding.

Once subject matter knowledge is in hand, there are still a number of obstacles to increasing the levels of quantitative literacy in the schools owing to tensions in the policy practices surrounding teacher education and licensure. Those most interested in increasing quantitative literacy in schools may themselves be divided on the degree to which they subscribe the adequacy or sufficiency of relying on naïve teaching to accomplish the task or the degree to which they would rely on the professional study and practice of teaching.

The Alternative of Reliance on Naïve Teaching

Nearly every reform report calls for an increase in the teacher's subject matter preparation at the expense of professional teacher education courses on the view that teaching is a naturally occurring human behavior, a wholly natural act that is an enduring and universal feature[5] of the repertoire of human behaviors. Humans are, in other words, a teaching species, a species whose young cannot, and do not, survive unless they are taught, invariably by persons with no formal schooling in teaching or in teacher education. Ashley and Tomasello (1998) found evidence of teaching in children as young as three years old, and

Strauss, Ziv, and Stein (2002) found that children's style of teaching a new board game or building something changed from demonstration and modeling at 3–4 years to predominately verbal explaining at five and six years. Seven year olds can adapt their teaching on occasion to their perception of their pupil's proficiency and knowledge. They also introduce the new teaching strategy of asking the learners if they understood, and they then adapt their *teaching* to the learners' mistakes. Children's pedagogy is also influenced by schooling itself. Maynard (2004) found that older Mayan children (6–11 years), who had been to school, were also able to adopt "school-like" teaching with their younger siblings (didactic teaching at a distance) in place of indigenous teaching practices used in families for cooking and weaving (close-up interactive demonstrations).

J. M. Stephens (1967) catalogued the features of naturally occurring teaching in his theory of spontaneous schooling. His argument was that schooling, a feature of all known anthropological groups,[6] was dependent on a set of natural human tendencies that some persons had in greater degrees than others. Those who had these tendencies in generous proportions would be seen, whether they intended to teach or not, as teachers by the members of their communities. Teaching and learning would take place naturally, spontaneously, non-deliberatively, and not necessarily with any particular motive or intention to benefit the pupil. They would occur merely because the tendencies, which fundamentally serve only the teacher's needs, led incidentally and inevitably to learning in those persons in the teacher's company. Teaching, in other words, was natural and spontaneous; it occurred whenever a person with these tendencies was with any other person for a protracted period, and it occurred to satisfy some need of the teacher, not some need of the student. It is not important that Stephen's speculations on the specific character of the natural or spontaneous tendencies are correct in every detail, but only that there are natural teaching abilities and that these seem to be adequate to account for most of the features of contemporary teaching and schooling.

The natural teaching view is also reinforced by the fact that many effective private school teachers have not taken education courses, nor have professors, who were trained only to research, not teach, their subjects (Judge, Lemosse, Paine, & Sedlak, 1994) and seemingly meet their teaching responsibilities satisfactorily without the benefit of engaging the content of education courses.

Some policy-makers raise the related question: Even if formal teacher education can refine and improve natural teaching somewhat, can the nation's needs for teachers still be met, less expensively and adequately, by the natural teaching techniques and styles we all seem to possess coupled with study in an appropriate academic major?

An Alternative to Naïve Teaching: Reliance on Pedagogical Education

The theory of spontaneous schooling, and the view of teaching that is based on it, have a number of problematical consequences for contemporary schooling because schooling now takes place on larger scales than that found in families and other anthropological groups, and because schooling increasingly takes place in circumstances where the teacher and the pupils have less and less in common. As a result, reliance on the theory of natural teaching can be expected to lead to serious pedagogical mistakes for both weak and superior students. Quite apart from the matter of scale and the degree of similarity between the teacher and the pupil, the theory promotes a direct mode of instruction that is unduly limiting in terms of modern views of cognition and cognitive development that support advances in quantitative literacy. Finally, the theory provides insufficient guidance for the solution of difficult and novel problems in schooling that go beyond the natural teacher's exclusive reliance on "*showing and telling*," the core of the natural style of teaching found in children and adults.

Low Expectations. When the teacher and the pupil are not alike and when the teacher may have lower expectations for the *different* pupil, the natural tendencies lead to very unfortunate consequences (Brophy & Good, 1986; Evertson, Hawley, & Zlotnick, 1985). When the teacher and the pupil have dissimilar backgrounds, we can expect the natural teaching mechanisms that support familial instruction will not operate to benefit the student.

Natural teaching leads to a predictable number of pedagogical mistakes that novices, and regrettably some licensed teachers, make unless they also have had the opportunity to learn and practice extensively some counterintuitive and *unnatural* teaching techniques. For example, it is certain that the natural teacher, well-meaning and well-read with good college grades, will still make the following pedagogical mistakes with their pupils for whom they have low expectations, regardless of how benignly they came to have these expectations. They will treat these pupils not as individuals but as a group, seat them further away and outside the classroom zone of frequent teacher-pupil interaction, look at them less, ask them low-level questions, call on them less often, give them less time to respond, give them fewer hints when they are called upon, and give them less praise and more blame than other pupils. And the natural teachers will do all this out of a mistaken sense of kindness that is seemingly oblivious to the pedagogical harm their undisciplined actions have caused their pupils (Hawley & Rosenholtz, 1984; Murray, 1996).

This untrained, natural, and kind person, believing the pupil does not know very much, will not want to embarrass the pupil by calling on the pupil often, will ask *appropriately* easy questions when the pupil is called upon, will give fewer hints and less time when the pupil fails to respond as it would be unkind to prolong the pupil's embarrassment and so on. The educated teacher, like all professionals, and in contrast with the *spontaneous* or *natural* teacher, must discipline many of his or her kinder instincts and implement an equitable and disciplined professional approach to bring about high levels of achievement from those pupils for whom the teacher would otherwise have low expectations (Oakes, 1985). These professional actions are frequently counterintuitive and as a result require extensive practice so that they can be performed by *second nature*.

Higher-order Forms of Learning Needed for Quantitative Literacy. Kantor & Lowe (2004) argue persuasively that historically the schools, with a few exceptions that proved the rule, were inattentive to quality education and higher order subject matter understanding of the sort expected in quantitative literacy. Teaching was largely *showing and telling* coupled with rapid fire teacher questions and student recitation and memorization, which while useful for the rote learning of some quantitative facts, limited higher level achievement and was a hallmark of the natural teaching regime.

A further limitation of the natural teaching regime, apart from the harm caused to weaker pupils over time, is that it does not take the superior pupil much beyond the kind of information that can be told and demonstrated and conforms to the stimulus-response and imitative forms of learning. While such declarative knowledge is important, the forms of quantitative literacy that are constructed by the pupil, not merely transmitted to the pupil, are increasingly seen as key to the student's performance at the advanced levels of the disciplines (Murray, 1992; Ogle, Alsalam, & Rogers, 1991). A pupil can be told and shown, for example, that A is greater than B, and that B is also greater than C, but an essential ingredient of quantitative reasoning, the knowledge that A *must be* greater than C, and that one could know that without ever looking directly at A and C, cannot be simply given to the pupil. Not only is A truly greater than C, but more than that, it *has to be* greater. The quantitative literacy notion of necessity has its origins elsewhere and outside the definitions in mathematics. Showing and telling have not been found, except in very unusual circumstances, to be effective means of "teaching" necessity (Beilin, 1971; Murray, 1978 & 1990; Smith, 1993). It is one thing to know that a statement is true, but quite another to know that it *must be* true. The origins of necessity, and other pivotal concepts, like irony or justice, seem to lie in *dialectical* instruction, which demands intellectual action on the part of the teacher and the student. While more demanding on the student, dialectic or maieutic teaching, is a less direct and more subtle form of instruction than that supported by the natural "*show and tell*" teaching tendencies.

The Naïve Theory of Mind. Along with the natural teaching techniques there often comes a naive and serviceable, but limited, theory of the human mind (Heider, 1958; Baldwin, 1980). The pupil's school performance in the naive or common sense theory is tied to four common place factors—ability, effort, task difficulty, and luck. With these four factors, the natural teacher can explain completely the pupil's success or failure on school tasks by attributing the level of the pupil's performance to his/her ability or effort, or to the difficulty of the school task, or to plain luck. The problem with naive theory, apart from the circularity in the four factors, is that more sophisticated theories have been developed in which it can be shown that ability, to take only one example, is not fixed or stable, and that it varies from moment to moment interactively with many other mental factors, not just the few in the naive theory (Baldwin, 1980; Murray, 1991). Naive theories, for example, see forgetting as the inevitable decay of stored knowledge, when the educated view is that forgetting is an active thinking process of interference and reorganization (Rose, 1993). Similarly misconceptions in science and mathematics are seen as the result of misinformation or forgetting when the educated view is that they stem from the lively interaction of the earlier, more primitive and well-established conceptual frameworks with later information (an imperfect balance between assimilation and accommodation in the Genevan sense (Baldwin, 1980)).

Naïve Pedagogy. Natural teaching is essentially *showing and telling* (see Olson and Bruner (1996) for an account of folk pedagogy). Naïve pedagogy is based upon a *transmission of intact packets of information* model of teaching. Strauss and Shilony (1994) interviewed experienced and novice science and humanities teachers about how they would teach a topic of their choosing to children of various ages (7-17 years). Both novice and regrettably many experienced teachers in each discipline conceptualized teaching only as the flow of information from their heads to their pupils' heads, acknowledging their own role was only to devise manageable and interesting ways of entry into the student's mind so the information could be stored and anchored appropriately. The student is passive, a receptacle waiting to be filled, and if the information fails to flow to its destination, the receptacle was taken to be too small and/or the student was inattentive.

Astington and Pelletier (1996) catalogued the following tenets of naïve pedagogy: (1) children are born with abilities and capacities that unfold linearly in time, (2) instructional sequences should match developmental sequences, (2) learning occurs sequentially within a hierarchy of skills, and (3) student errors are attributable to incomplete learning or inattention. When the pupil needs to do something, the teacher need only demonstrate or model it, and when the pupil needs to learn something, the teacher need only tell the pupil what they need to know.

On the whole, these folk or naïve pedagogical techniques and beliefs frustrate the modern pedagogies based on dialectic, discovery, invention and collaboration that would be tuned to enhancing quantitative literacy. They are also at variance with some contemporary research findings: developmental pathways, for example, are rarely linear and often show fits and starts, oscillations, and even reversals, particularly when performance is at an optimal level or when a new skill is being developed (Fischer & Bidell, 1998).

These naive views of how the mind works coupled with equally naive views about the nature of the academic subject matters as received and objective truth further limit the benefits that can be expected from nonprofessional or natural teaching (see Amsler and Stotko (1996), for examples of the possible and legitimate variations in what constitutes correct subject matter knowledge). The naive view of subject matter also shows itself principally in the area of assessment of the student's understanding of a subject matter.

Classroom Assessment. The natural or naïve teacher's evaluation of the pupil's correct and incorrect responses provides a telling and targeted arena for distinguishing naive and educated teachers. A student's reasoning may look illogical to a naive teacher, while the educated teacher will see that the student's reasoning is intact, but has operated on different premises from those of the set problem. The naive teacher will be distressed when a pupil who had pluralized *mouse* correctly suddenly pluralizes it as *mouses,* while the educated teacher will see the new plural, not as an unfortunate regression, but as a positive sign of cognitive advancement in which the pupil is exhibiting a newly developed appreciation of a linguistic rule that is merely over-generalized in this instance.

Other decrements in performance may also indicate educational progress; some six year old pupils not only maintain incorrectly that the longer row of two rows of five beans has more beans, but also maintain that the longer row must have more beans and would always have more beans. These errors occur even after the pupil has just counted the equal number of beans in each row. It happens that the error, "there *must* be more beans," which seems the more serious error, is indicative of more developed reasoning than the error, "there are more beans" (Murray & Zhang, 2005). Naturally, it is very difficult for the naive or natural teacher to accept any error or poor performance as a marker of progress, yet the failure to see some errors as markers of progress is another serious pedagogical mistake that stems from the naive theory of teaching and learning (see Bruner, 1961 on *creative errors*).

The student's superior performance may also be misinterpreted by the naïve teacher (see Strauss & Stavey, 1982 for examples where correct performance actually rests on immature and incorrect reasoning). Murray (1990) found that young children's success on a developmentally advanced quantitative reasoning task (the classic wine and water mixture problem) was, despite the appearances, not an indication of the same level of cognitive development as older children's success on the same task. The adolescents seemingly and inappropriately coded the problem as a probability problem and reasoned to an indeterminate conclusion when in fact outcome is a matter of necessity—there must be as much wine in the water in one glass as water in the wine of the other glass.

If a child arrives at the correct answer to a multiplication problem through serial addition, how would the naïve teacher score the response—as superior or inferior to the response of a child who arrives at an incorrect answer through multiplication? Do college students, who correctly calculate the mean, median, and mode, operate at different standards of sophistication if their reasoning is based on a calculation algorithm, a mechanical model of balance, an algebraic deduction, or a special case in the calculus? Upon what theory, and by what means, would the naïve teacher determine whether some solutions are more sophisticated, elegant, significant, and so forth, than other solutions. By what criteria would the teacher even see his/her teaching as successful and/or high quality (see Fenstermacher & Richardson, 2005 on these distinctions)?

The naïve or educated teacher's mistakes in subject matter knowledge and its assessment are a problem under any view of teacher employment. Additional study in the subject matter would seem the obvious remedy, and nearly every reform initiative in teacher education, as noted earlier, recommends additional and deeper subject matter preparation. The exact nature of the study, however, has been shown to be complex (Wilson, Floden, & Ferrini-Mundy, 2001; Rice, 2003; Floden & Meniketti, 2005). Generally more preparation in the subject, particularly mathematics, is positively related the state's assessment of student learning, but there are inconsistencies in which additional subject matter preparation sometimes weakens student learning (Rice, 2003). The state assessments are, of course, about relatively narrow and easily scored concepts of quantitative literacy.

The Problem of Abbreviated Study. The research on the efficacy of pedagogical courses is weaker than that for subject matter courses, but also shows some positive association with student teaching (Rice, 2003). It is doubtful that a sufficient level of pedagogical training can be reached in a short period. For example, on a simple reading of Skinner, as might be found in a survey course in education, prospective teachers could believe that positive reinforcement (or reward) is an effective and preferred way to increase the likelihood of desirable pupil behavior. Without an awareness of the important exceptions and qualifications in which rewards actually weaken a response (the *over-justification phenomenon*), teachers will make mistakes by implementing procedures that run counter to their intentions (Cameron & Pierce, 1994)[7].

Similarly, upon a quick reading, the prospective teacher could come to believe that student grades should be normally distributed or that reliability is a property of a test rather than a property of those who took the test. These professional lessons cannot be easily abridged or rushed because many educational innovations are counterintuitive and subtly tied to hidden factors.

For example, it makes a difference whether addition problems, like $8+5=\_\_$, are presented horizontally or vertically. While a seven-year-old pupil, to take another example, may understand that the amount of clay in a ball would be unaffected if the ball were flattened into a pancake, she would more than likely believe incorrectly that the same pancake would weigh more and take up less space, despite the fact that the she had claimed the ball and pancake have the same amount of clay. In fact it is only in adolescence that she would understand that the volume of the ball and pancake were the same. Furthermore, it is now acknowledged that many research findings are inherently provisional and must be qualified by context and the cohort or generation of pupils who participated in the study, as different results are obtained from different cohorts and contexts on such basic questions as whether intellectual performance decreases after a certain age. Thus, having studied the research literature at one time is not a guarantee that the results can be applied at a later time with regard to such nagging and recurring issues as social promotion, skipping grades, ability grouping, optimal class size, delayed instruction, and so forth. Current and deeper study is required throughout the teaching career.

The Problem of Insufficient Time. Sudden or effortless changes in behavior are taken by developmental psychologists as a sign that the change was not fundamental, but rather a temporary change, caused by a peripheral mechanism (e.g., fatigue, inattention, misperception, etc.), and not authentic. Protracted and extended practice and experience is needed to overcome the acquisitions of a prior stage of development or of the naïve or natural teaching regime, which seems to be deeply rooted in behavior.

Smith (1989) has shown that highly motivated, knowledgeable, and experienced teachers were still unsure and shaky after ten months of practice in their efforts to implement a *conceptual change* science teaching technique, even though they practiced the new technique extensively under ideal teacher education conditions (extended coaching one on one). Such protracted experience is rarely afforded in the traditional teacher education program. Despite having practiced the technique in a variety of settings, having video and stimulated recall analysis of their teaching performance, and having personal feedback of their efforts, the teachers regressed to their earlier teaching style whenever the lesson took an unusual and unexpected turn (Smith & Neale, 1990). Their regression to *show and tell* sometimes undermined the entire point of quantitative reasoning itself, because the teachers would deny or ignore an unexpected outcome in a demonstration in favor of the outcome that was supposed to have happened. In a light and shadow lesson, when a single shadow was expected and predicted, but a double shadow appeared, the teacher would deny it or ignore it and continue with the demonstration as if the single predicted and expected shadow had appeared, all in opposition to the new teaching technique.

The classic defense against this kind of *regression under stress* to the more primitive and older strategies is *over-learning* or practice well-beyond what is needed to simply learn the new skill or approach. Regrettably, few teacher education programs can make the necessary provisions for over-learning.

Olson and Bruner (1996) conclude that the shift from the simplest pedagogies of natural teaching to the more sophisticated ones available in scholarship entails a focus on what the student, not the teacher can do, on what the student thinks, on the student's view of teaching itself, and on knowledge as an emergent event in the dialectic between the teacher and the student.

Weak Protocols for Quality Assurance in Teaching. Ironically, the calibration of teacher certification and more ambitious goals for teachers of quantitative literacy is held back by the very fact that teaching has all the attributes of the other professions—accreditation, professional associations, standardized tests, licenses and credentials, advanced degrees, and so forth. While there is some fragile evidence for the efficacy of the license in the teaching field and advanced degrees (Rice, 2003), none of these requirements, all demanding in their appearance, has much credibility within or outside the profession as each is routinely waived when there are shortages of otherwise qualified persons for the public schools. In the case of the private schools, many states typically set and require no standards at all, a practice that only reinforces the lack of standing the current standards have.

To take one example of the low regard in which these bureaucratic standards are held, the National Board for Professional Teaching Standards (NBPTS), departing from the practice of other professional national boards, elected *not* to require a degree in teacher education, a state teaching license, or study at an accredited institution for those permitted to sit for its certification examinations. National Board certification, itself, is not even required for advancement in the field or promotion to higher levels of professional responsibility.

Since 1951 all states must give their permission (a license) for a person to teach in a public school, and a few also require the license for private school teaching. Historically and continuing to current time, three factors have been relied on in granting this permission—(1) an assessment of the prospective teacher's character, (2) the prospective teacher's tested knowledge (particularly of the teaching subject), and/or (3) the prospective teacher's teaching skill as attested to by the completion of a higher education program of study in pedagogy.

The state's granting of formal permission to teach is meant to be based on indicators that permit an overall prediction that a particular candidate will perform safely and satisfactorily in the complex situation of teaching. Upon which of the three factors the various states elect to award their license depends on whether they see teaching as a profession based exclusively upon specialized university-level study, or whether they see teaching as little more than a civil servant's line of work that can be taken up by nearly any well-meaning person who has mastered a subject matter.

One issue, both historically and at present, centers on these competing views of teaching—how a person learns to teach, who should be entitled to teach, and more importantly who should be prohibited from teaching, whether teaching is inherently moral or technical, an art or a science, and so forth. Recently, policy-makers have wanted also to know whether any of these factors influence the performance of the prospective teacher's students on the standards-based assessments the state makes of pupil and student achievement. No matter the basis of the license award, the students of licensed teachers generally perform slightly higher on state tests than the students of non-licensed teachers.

A second issue centers on who has the authority and expertise to grant the license. While it is essentially a settled matter today that the states have this authority, it was not always a settled matter because local communities, the profession, individuals, and the colleges have battled for the right to make the determination, and today some argue that licensure should be granted only at the national level in accordance with national standards.

From colonial times onward, parents, school boards, personnel directors, state superintendents, policy-makers and their counterparts have sought an answer to the question of what will predict who, among all the available candidates for a teaching position, is likely to succeed and perhaps more urgently who is likely to fail in the position.

Regrettably, all that is really available to them in their quest of a way to determine who should be permitted to teach is a set of flawed measures. A collection of flawed and incomplete indicators can be useful and one of the most correlated measures, *IQ*, is itself little more than a systematic combination of other limited measures, like memory span, word meaning and fluency, spatial relations, manual dexterity, classification, numerical reasoning, reaction time, common knowledge, which by themselves have little predictive validity. Each is weak and flawed in its power to account for very much of human behavior, although the compilation of these separate component measures is significantly related to nearly all aspects of human intellectual accomplishment.

Unfortunately, the historical and current desire for a simple, single, and inexpensive measure of teaching potential yields risky answers that would be as silly as using spatial relations skill or reaction time as the sole indicator of intelligence.

Historically, the prevailing 18th century tests of good character (basically interviews with local clergy) were supplanted by local tests of subject matter and pedagogy in the 19th century, and when these proved to be biased, invalid, and easily corrupted, they in turn were replaced by diplomas and degrees from programs of study in the newly emerging normal schools in the late 19th and early 20th centuries. The 1980's saw a resurgence of tests of basic skills and subject matter coupled with the academic degree, but some, like the American Board for the Certification of Teacher Excellence (ABCTE), promote a stand alone subject matter test as a sufficient basis for gauging teacher competence and potential.

The recurring dissatisfaction with the nation's schools, prompts non-reflective policy-makers and some of the reform-minded, to simply reject the indicator of the moment—the education degree on one occasion is replaced or supplemented with a standardized test because schools of education, even accredited ones, give degrees to some academically weak students. Tests of uncertain psychometric merit are then relied upon, and historically were relied on exclusively until the 1920's, when it was clear then as now that the tests' validity coefficients are low or absent. Direct classroom observation of a sample of the candidate's teaching, while closer to the predictive task at hand, proves unduly burdensome when properly done. Because the number of observations needed to reach acceptable reliability levels is nearly identical with the entire first year teaching assignment itself, predictive observational measures of teaching are essentially redundant with the very behavior they were put in place to predict.

Currently, there are about eight potential ingredients in the nation's system of quality assurance, all admittedly insufficient by themselves, but collectively they permit tolerable levels of accurate prediction of teacher success, each one speaking to a different aspect of teacher quality. These eight interrelated ingredients are: the degree in teacher education, accreditation[8], state program approval, the teaching license, national board certification, tenure, license tests, and the achievement of the teacher's pupils itself. While some of these eight indicators or measures may by themselves lead to a correct prediction of effective teaching, each is subject to known distortions that may lead to an inaccurate prediction; that is, they may indicate that a person can teach well or at an acceptable level, when in fact the person will prove to be inept with some pupils in some challenging circumstances.

In matters of importance, where mistakes have significant societal costs, prudence and common sense commend systems of checks and balances supported by multiple measures. A sound prediction that a prospective teacher will succeed might rest on the person's completion of a state approved degree program from an accredited institution coupled with performance on standardized tests of subject matter and pedagogy coupled with demonstrations of teaching that incorporated measures of pupil performance. The prediction is enhanced through interview techniques that seek to establish that prospective teacher possesses attitudinal characteristics, values, beliefs, and expectations that align with those possessed by veteran successful teachers.

The logic of convergence as a strategy for building a credible prediction out of individually weak and flawed measures requires that the measures contributing to the prediction be multiple and independent. Efforts that conflate measures or have one substitute for the other introduce unwarranted risk. The initial driver's license, for example, requires a road test in which the candidate demonstrates proficiency in the task itself. There would be considerable risk if the road test were waived solely on the basis of good grades in accredited or approved driver's education courses, or high marks on a written test of knowledge about driving. Rather, the state seeks to reduce the risk of granting a license to substandard drivers by requiring independent and multiple sources of evidence about the candidate's driving (a sample of driving behavior, a written test of driving knowledge, and driver's education or experience).

Very nearly the opposite approach has evolved for teaching. First, the license is often not required for certain teaching assignments – for private school teachers, or tutors, or others who work outside the public schools. It is waived now for about 5% of the public school workforce. It would be unthinkable to waive the drivers' licenses or require it only for those who drive publicly owned vehicles or require medical licenses only for those physicians who work in public hospitals and clinics. Program approval and accreditation are frequently collapsed into one assessment and in some scenarios the license test may substitute for all other indicators together, thereby losing all the power of convergence.

The effort to increase the levels of quantitative literacy in the schools will surely fail unless each of these elements in the quality assurance system is addressed and coordinated. Change in education, historically, can come through the manipulation of one or two of these quality assurance devices, but these changes are typically short-lived and disappointing. Lasting change begins with a clear conception of the measurable features of *numeracy,* the establishment of a course of study along the lines of the options for a new academic major described earlier, the specifications of new requirements for the teaching license, the redesign of license tests, recognition in the accreditation and state approval standards, and incorporation in the state's curriculum assessments. Without this clear conception, the policy levers provided by teacher education, licensing, credentialing, accreditation are relatively powerless to provide a structure that will directly encourage and reward a teacher who has the capacity to pursue Sean's conjectures.

References

Amsler, M. & Stotko, E. M. (1996). Changing the subject: teacher education and language arts. In F. Murray (Ed.), *The teacher educator's handbook* (pp. 194–216). San Francisco, CA: Jossey-Bass.

Astington, J. W. & Pelletier, J. (1996). The language of mind. In D.R. Olson & N. Torrance (Eds.), *The handbook of education and human development* (pp. 591–619). Oxford, UK: Blackwell.

Ashley, J. & Tomasello, M. (1998). Cooperative problem solving and teaching in preschoolers. *Social Development, 7,* 143–163.

Baldwin, A. (1980). *Theories of child development (2nd edition).* New York, NY: John Wiley & Sons.

Ball, D. (1991). Teaching mathematics for understanding: What do teachers need to know about subject matter? In M. Kennedy (Ed.), *Teaching academic subjects to diverse learners* (pp.63–83). New York, NY: Teachers College Press.

Beilin, H. (1971). The training and acquisition of logical operations. In Rosskopf, et al. (Eds.), *Piagetian cognitive-development research and mathematical education* (pp. 81–124). Washington, D.C.: National Council of Teachers of Mathematics, Inc.

Brophy, J. & Good, T. (1986). Teacher behavior and student achievement. In M. Wittrock (Ed.), *Handbook of research on teaching, 3rd edition* (pp. 328–375). New York, NY: Macmillan.

Bruner, J. (1961). *The process of education.* Cambridge, MA: Harvard University Press.

Cameron, J. & Pierce, D. (1994). Reinforcement, reward, and intrinsic motivation: a meta-analysis. *Review of Educational Research, 64,* No. 3, 363–423.

Crosby, A. (1997). *The measure of reality: quantification and western society 1250-1600.* New York, NY: Cambridge University Press.

Evertson, C., Hawley, W., & Zlotnick, M. (1985). Making a difference in educational quality through teacher education. *Journal of Teacher Education,* 36(3), 2–12.

Draper, P. (1976). Docail and economic constraints on child life among the !Kung. In B. Lee & I. Devore (Eds.), *Kahlahari hunter-gatherers* (pp. 199–217). Cambridge, MA: Harvard University Press.

Fensternacher, G. D. & Richardson, V. (2005). On making determinations of quality teaching. *Teachers College Record, 107(1),* 186–213.

Ferrari, M. & Sternberg, R. (1998). The development of mental abilities and style. In D. Kuhn & R. Siegler (Eds.), *Handbook of child psychology: cognition, perception, and language, fifth edition, volume two* (pp. 899-946). New York, NY: John Wiley & Sons.

Fischer, K., & Bidell, T. (1998). Dynamic development of psychological structures in action and thought. In W. Damon (Ed.) and R. Lerner (Vol. Ed.), *Handbook of child psychology (Volume I)* (pp. 467–561). New York, NY: John Wiley & Sons.

Floden, R. E. & Meniketti, M. (2005). Research on the effects of coursework in the arts and sciences in the foundations of education. In M Cochran-Smith and K Zeichner (Eds.), *Studying teacher education* (pp. 251–308). Rawah, NJ: Lawrence Erlbaum & Associates.

Hawley, W. & Rosenholtz, S. (1984). Good schools: what research says about improving student achievement. *Peabody Journal of Education, 61 (4)* 1–178.

Heider, F. (1958). *The psychology of interpersonal relations.* New York, NY: John Wiley & Sons.

Judge, H., Lemosse, M., Paine, M., & Sedlak, M. (1994). *Oxford studies in comparative education, Vol. 4 (1&2): The university and the teachers.* Wallingford, UK: Triangle Books.

Kantor, H. & Lowe, R. (2204). Reflections on history and quality education. *Educational Researcher, 33(5),* 6–10.

Konner, M. (1976). Maternal care, infant behavior and development among the !Kung. In B. Lee & I. Devore (Eds.), *Kahlahari hunter-gatherers* (pp. 218–245). Cambridge, MA: Harvard University Press.

Maynard, A. (2004). Cultures of teaching in childhood: Formal schooling and Maya sibling teaching at home. *Cognitive Development, 19,* 517–535.

McDiarmid, G. W. (1992). The arts and sciences as preparation for teaching. *Issue Paper 92-3,* E. Lansing, MI: National Center for Research on Teacher Learning.

Murray, F. (1978). Teaching strategies and conservation training. In A. M. Lesgold, J.W. Pellegrino, S. Fokkema, & R. Glaser, (Eds.), *Cognitive psychology and instruction* (pp. 419–428). New York, NY: Plenum.

Murray, F. (1990). The conversion of truth into necessity. In W. Overton (Ed.), *Reasoning, necessity and logic: Developmental perspectives* (pp. 183–204). Hillsdale, NJ: Lawrence Erlbaum Associates.

Murray, F. (1990). The conversion of truth into necessity. In W. Overton (Ed.), *Reasoning, necessity & logic: Developmental perspectives*, (pp. 183–203). Hillsdale, NJ: Lawrence Erlbaum Associates.

Murray, F. (1991). Alternative conceptions of academic knowledge for prospective elementary teachers. In M. Pugach and H. Barnes (Eds.), *Changing the practice of teacher education: The role of the knowledge base* (pp. 63–82), Washington, DC: AACTE.

Murray, F. (1992). Restructuring and constructivism: the development of American educational reform. In H. Beilin and P. Pufall (Eds.), *Piaget's theory: prospects and possibilities* (pp. 287–308). Hillsdale, NJ: Lawrence Erlbaum Associates.

Murray, F (1996) Beyond natural teaching: The case for professional education. In F. B. Murray (Ed.), *The teacher educator's handbook,*. San Francisco, CA: Jossey-Bass. 3–13

Murray, F. & Zhang, Y. (2005). The role of necessity in cognitive development. *Cognitive Development, 20,* 235–241.

Oakes, J. (1985). *Keeping track: How schools structure inequality.* New Haven, CT: Yale University Press.

Ogle, L., Alsalam, N., & Rogers, G. (1991). *The condition of education 1991,* Washington, DC: National Center for Educational Statistics.

Ohanian, S. (1999). *One size fits few: the folly of educational standards.* New York, NY: Heinemann.

Ohanian, S. (2000). Goals 200: What's in a name? *Phi delta Kappan, vol. 81 (5),* 345–355.

Olson, D & Bruner, J. (1996). Folk psychology and folk pedagogy. In D.R. Olson & N. Torrance (Eds.), *The handbook of education and human development* (pp. 9–27). Oxford, UK: Blackwell.

Premack, D. & Premack, A. J. (1996). Why animals lack pedagogy and some cultures have more of it than others. In D.R. Olson & N. Torrance (Eds.), *The handbook of education and human development* (pp. 302–323). Oxford, UK: Blackwell.

Raths, J. (1999). A consumer's guide to teacher standards. *Phi Delta Kappan, vol. 81 (3),* 136–142.

Rice, J. K. (2003). *Teacher quality: understanding the effectiveness of teacher attributes.* Washington, DC: Economic Policy Institute.

Rose, S. (1993). *The making of memory.* New York, NY: Anchor Books.

Rushcamp, S. and Roehler, L. (1992). Characteristics supporting change in a professional development school. *Journal of teacher education,* 43 (1), 19–27.

Smith, D. (1989). *The role of teacher knowledge in teaching conceptual change science lessons.* Unpublished doctoral dissertation, University of Delaware.

Smith, D. and Neal, D. (1990). The construction of subject matter in primary science teaching. In J. Brophy (Ed.), *Advances in research on teaching subject matter knowledge* (vol 2, pp. 187–243). Greenwich, CT: JAI Press.

Smith, L. (1993). *Necessary knowledge: Piagetian perspectives on constructivism.* Hillsdale, NJ: Lawrence Erlbaum & Associates.

Steen, L. (1990). (Ed.). *On the shoulders of giants: New approaches to numeracy.* Washington, DC: National Academy Press.

Stephens, John (1967). *The process of schooling: a psychological examination.* New York, NY: Holt, Rinehart & Winston.

Strauss, S. & Silhoney, T. (1994). Teachers' models of children's mind and leaning: Implications for teacher education. In L.A. Hirschfeld and S. A. Gelman (Eds.), *Mapping the mind: Domain specificity in cognition and culture* (pp. 455-473). New York, NY: Cambridge University Press.

Straus, S, Ziv, M. & Stein, A. (2002). Teaching as a natural cognition and its relation to preschoolers' developing theory of mind. *Child Development, 17,* 1473–1487.

Strauss, S. & Ziv, M. (2004). Teaching: Ontogenesis, culture, and education. *Cognitive development,* 19, 451–456.

Tyson, H. (1994). *Who will teach the children: Progress and resistance in teacher education.* New York, NY: Jossey-Bass.

Wilson, S. M, Floden, R. E., Ferrini-Mundy, J. (2001). Teacher preparation research: Current knowledge, gaps, and recommendations. Seattle, WA: University of Washington, Center for the Study of Teaching and Policy.

Wynn, K. (1992). Addition and subtraction by human infants. *Nature, 358,* 749–750.

Endnotes

[1] Based on an episode in Deborah Ball's teaching as a professor of mathematics education in the Michigan State University School of Education who also taught third grade mathematics each day in East Lansing.

[2] It requires understanding of the number system, a repertoire of mathematical techniques, and an inclination and ability to solve quantitative or spatial problems in a range of contexts

[3] Ball, D. (1991) found that not only were mathematics and non-math majors no better at finding examples of the division of 1¾ by the fraction ½, but their offered examples were often wrong mathematically. They tended to give examples where the division was by 2 rather than ½.

[4] Prior to this level understanding, adolescents will argue that while setting the clock ahead in the spring makes one truly older, the effect is cancelled later when the hour is lost, so age is in the end unchanged.

[5] Draper (1976) and Konner (1976) show there are complex limits to universality of teaching in anthropological groups. In some cultures children are taught to eat but not to sit and to walk and vice versa in other cultures.

[6] Premack & Premack (1996, p. 315) point out that "pedagogy is not an official anthropological category: no catalogue lists the pedagogical practices of different groups … the anthropology of pedagogy is largely nonexistent; its proper study has yet to begin."

[7] See further comment on the over-justification phenomenon in the Spring, 1996 issue of the *Review of Educational Research, 66,* No. 1, 1–51.

[8] In the 1998 a newly established accreditor, the Teacher Education Accreditation Council (TEAC), shifted the basis of accreditation to the evidence that the graduates were competent beginning teachers, and the older accreditor, the National Council for the Accreditation of Teacher Education (NCATE), followed suite so that accreditation is now centered on evidence of the prospective teacher's understanding and skill. Only half the nation's teacher education programs are accredited.

Workshop Discussions

Institutional Audit Questions

One anticipated outcome of the Wingspread conference Quantitative Literacy and Its Implications for Teacher Education was a list of questions that could help schools and colleges evaluate their programs in QL and teacher education. Questions for this "institutional audit" were solicited from conference participants in advance of the conference, and an edited list was distributed and discussed at the conference. Questions address both the nature of QL and two types of institutions: schools and school districts where teachers teach, and colleges and universities where teachers are prepared.

The following is this list of institutional audit questions interspersed with observations from conference participants offered in reaction to the discussions.

General questions:

- What are the basic quantitative requirements for all future teachers? Is there a common core of basic QL that applies to all subjects and all grades, and thus to all teachers?

On QL and Social Science . . .

QL, especially as it concerns informed citizenship, can be centered in the social sciences or social studies at the post-secondary and secondary levels. If we are concerned for the contextual validity and meaning of numerical challenges, why not teach QR in those contexts in which it naturally falls rather than in the form of problems to which context is appended?

Relatedly, the reporter advanced the provocative claim that mathematics is as important to QR as informational literacy. In the contemporary web-based world, arguably, the greatest QL challenge isn't generating and evaluating numbers mathematically, it's finding existing numbers and thinking about presented numbers knowledgeably and critically.

— Neil Lutsky, reporter

- Is it desirable (or even possible) to make a clear distinction between basic quantitative literacy appropriate for all teachers and higher order thinking that may be more appropriate for some grades or subjects than for others?

- Is a teacher's mastery of QL adequate preparation for teaching quantitative skills essential for the life and work of students?

- What proportion of K–12 teachers believe that some form of QL is relevant to their teaching in that it complements rather than competes with existing content?

- To what extent do national documents that provide curricular guidelines support the role of QL in different subjects? Can you give examples where this is done well (or poorly)?

- Do you know of any exemplary materials suitable for helping teachers learn how to prepare students to be quantitatively literate?

- Is there conflict between traditional school mathematics and the mathematics needed for QR/QL in contemporary society?

- What are the special QL requirements for teachers of mathematics, science and social science?

On QL and Teacher Education . . .

From the teacher education perspective, experienced teachers are more likely to be able to handle the classroom instructional and assessment demands of QL instruction which will often go beyond single class periods or even units.

It is possible that the processes sought in QL tasks can be highlighted within a "senior level" mathematics course for all students, and in particular for those not aggressively pursuing the calculus sequence.

— Henry S. Kepner, Jr.
NCTM President-Elect

On Numeracy and Statistics . . .

I am convinced that numeracy has a rather large overlap with statistics education, especially as the latter is being defined and developed for the K–12 mathematics curriculum.

A project that would look at constructive and practical ways to combine the statistics education goals and the QL education goals, and to embed them into teacher education programs, could go a long way toward establishing QL as an integral part of the school curriculum. The current academic year (2007–08) would be a great time to start, as the NCTM professional development focus of the year is "Becoming Certain about Uncertainty: Data Analysis and Probability."

— Richard Scheaffer
Former President, ASA

- Is it possible to develop consensus of performance competence in QL appropriate to different educational levels (e.g., high school graduation, college graduation, teacher preparation)?

Institutional questions:

- Is QL/QR (e.g., the ability to use mathematics in everyday life) included in the learning goals for students at your institution? If so, how do you assess this goal?

- Does your district or college explicitly recognize QL as an area of professional preparation and development for teachers in all subjects and all grades? If so, how is this preparation and development carried out?

- Have the distinctions between mathematics and QL/QR been addressed in your required studies for future teachers?

> **On Institutional Audits . . .**
>
> *Experience has shown that when asked (during the course of an audit) some faculty may not know if the courses that they teach have a quantitative component. This seems to be the case in statistics where faculty in the past have said they 'don't know' if what they are teaching has a QL component of not.*
>
> — Kenneth C. Carr, reporter
> Reporting on Institutional Audit Panel

K–12 questions:

- What resources (e.g., experienced staff) does your school make available to assist teachers seeking to expand assignments and course modules in QL directions?

- In what ways do your hiring and new-teacher orientation encourage faculty in teaching QL and other cross-disciplinary goals (as opposed to seeing themselves as responsible only for a particular subject or grade)?

- Do your classroom materials (textbooks and supplements) support QL in the curriculum? Does your district provide supplementary materials that encourage QL-type problem solving? Are these materials easy for teachers to use? Do your teachers use them?

- Many QL problems invite creativity on the part of students, e.g., in questions they propose, in assumptions they make, or their approach to a solution. What kind of training experiences do you provide to help teachers who are more comfortable with a chalk/talk approach to explore these types of problems?

- How do your teachers assess the QL skills of their students?

Higher education questions:

- How are your learning goals for future teachers influenced by the need for them to teach quantitative literacy?
- Do your continuing education courses for teachers have any QL content?
- Where in your teacher preparation program do prospective teachers learn to tackle non-routine tasks that require QL thinking? ("Non-routine" refers to tasks for which nothing closely similar has been taught.)
- Are such non-routine QL-like tasks routinely included in tests and other course assessments?
- Where in your teacher preparation program do prospective teachers learn how to teach students to tackle non-routine tasks that require QL thinking?
- How can an undergraduate institution gain commitment from faculty across disciplines to take QL seriously as part of most regular liberal arts courses?

On Fractions I ...

We need to ensure that students recognize that there are many ways of conceiving of fractions and precisely because fractions (and ratios, decimals, and percentages) require shifting view points, they make excellent quantitative literacy (QL) tools.

On Fractions II ...

While fractions are critical in cooking, for most real-world applications and representations of quantitative evidence in the media, percentages are the key. Representing parts of a whole, comparing values to one another, measuring changes over time, scaling, and computing weighted averages all require a strong understanding of percentages.

— Corrine Taylor

- How can teacher preparation programs develop effective opportunities for future teachers to purposefully teach for QL outcomes?
- Do courses for future teachers in education, social sciences and humanities include quantitative reasoning tasks? How are these tasks connected to tasks in mathematics or science classes for these same students?
- Where in your curricula do students (especially future teachers) learn to (a) use of numbers in argument, (b) visually display quantitative information, and (c) write with precision, especially in the use of quantitative expressions? What evidence do you have that your graduates are achieving these goals?

- Do quantitative courses for future teachers include contemporary quantitative issues such as economic indices?
- Do your quantitative courses teach methods and algorithms or reasoning and problem solving? How do you know?
- What steps have been taken to coordinate cross curricular studies that support habits of mind such as quantitative literacy?
- Are the mathematics and statistics courses required of future teachers different from (a) those required of science and engineering students, or (b) those required for general education? If so, in what ways do they differ? How are these differences related to achieving or teaching QL?
- How can we assess QL competence in ways that both signal to students what is expected and provide useful formative feedback?
- Is it possible to add QL to an already over-prescribed context of teacher preparation?

List of Participants
with Institutional Affiliation at time of Conference

Joel Best
Professor of Sociology and Criminal Justice, University of Delaware

Richelle (Rikki) Blair
President-Elect, American Mathematical Association of Two-Year Colleges

Lloyd Bond
Senior Scholar, Carnegie Foundation for the Advancement of Teaching

Sadie Bragg
Senior Vice President, Borough of Manhattan Community College

Hugh Burkhardt
Professor and Director, Shell Center for Mathematical Education, University of Nottingham

Kenneth C. Carr
Professor and Assistant Dean, College of Education, Zayed University

Peter Ewell
Vice President, National Center for Higher Education Management Systems

Nathan D. Grawe
Assistant Professor of Economics, Carleton College

Richard Hersh
Co-Director, College Learning Assessment, Council for Aid to Education

Deborah Hughes Hallett
Professor of Mathematics, University of Arizona and Adjunct Professor of Public Policy, Kennedy School of Government, Harvard University.

Stanley Katz
Lecturer with the rank of Professor in the Woodrow Wilson School, Princeton University

Hank Kepner
Professor in Curriculum & Instruction and Mathematical Sciences, University of Wisconsin-Milwaukee, and President-Elect, National Council of Teachers of Mathematics

Joan R. Leitzel
President Emerita, University of New Hampshire

W. James "Jim" Lewis
Professor of Mathematics and Director of the Center for Science, Mathematics, and Computer Education, University of Nebraska-Lincoln

Neil Lutsky
William R. Kenan, Jr. Professor of Psychology, Carleton College

Bernard L. Madison
Professor of Mathematics, University of Arkansas

Jon Manon
Professor and Director, Mathematics and Science Education Resource Center, School of Education, University of Delaware

William G. McCallum
University Distinguished Professor of Mathematics, University of Arizona

Robert Orrill
Executive Director, National Council on Education and the Disciplines

Terrel L. Rhodes
Vice President, Association of American Colleges and Universities

Juana Sanchez
Director, International Statistical Literacy Project of the International Association for Statistical Education

Richard L. Scheaffer
Professor Emeritus of Statistics, University of Florida

Milo A. Schield
Professor of Business Administration and Director of the W. M. Keck Statistical Literacy Project, Augsburg College

Marla Schnall
High School Mathematics Teacher, Fairfax County Public Schools

Richard J. Shavelson
Margaret Jack Professor of Education and Professor of Psychology, Stanford University

Lynn Arthur Steen

Special Assistant to the Provost and Professor of Mathematics, St. Olaf College

William G. Steenken

Retired Engineer, General Electric Aviation

Corrine Taylor

Assistant Professor of Economics and Director of the Quantitative Reasoning Program, Wellesley College

Alan Tucker

S.U.N.Y. Distinguished Teaching Professor, Applied Mathematics and Statistics, State University of New York-Stony Brook

H.L. (Len) Vacher

Professor of Geology, University of South Florida

Arthur VanderVeen

Executive Director of College Readiness, The College Board